Wet Wickets and Dusty Balls

Wet Wickets
and Dusty Balls

A DIARY OF A CRICKETING YEAR

by

IAN MILLER

HAMISH HAMILTON · LONDON

First published in Great Britain 1986
by Hamish Hamilton Ltd
Garden House 57-59 Long Acre London WC2E 9JZ

British Library Cataloguing in Publication Data

Miller, Ian, *1952—*
   Wet wickets and dusty balls : a diary of a
   cricketing year.
   I. Title
   823′.914[F]   PR6063.I37/
   ISBN 0-241-11830-1

Filmset by Pioneer, Perthshire
Printed in Great Britain by
St Edmundsbury Press, Bury St Edmunds, Suffolk

For Zahzer

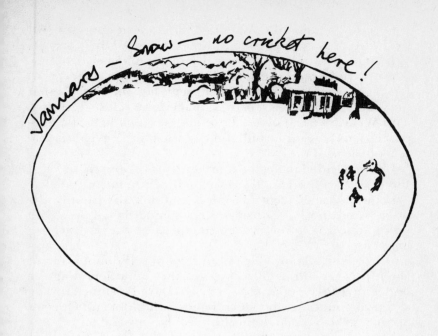

January — Snow — no cricket here!

Saturday 1st January 1983
I have decided to keep a diary for the first time in my adult life. I am concerned that this same adult life is slipping past with nothing to mark each *year*, let alone each week or day. A term starts, a year starts, one group of students has crossed the Styx, another settles itself on this bank. I am another year older and yet I have little to show. *All this will change.* I will keep a diary; a hooded boatman's log.

For, as they say, the record, my name is George Lyall, I'm thirty-eight and a history lecturer at Mugsborough College, a sixth-form college in a small town (Mugsborough, no less) close to Bristol. I have a wife, a Ford Cortina, a Barclaycard and a semi-detached house . . . a semi-attached house as I laughingly refer to it.

I don't dislike teaching. (I don't like it either.) I have a friendly, jocular relationship with my students which I'm careful to foster. I like my students and I care to let them know it . . . though I also ensure our relationship is workmanlike.

1

Even as I write 'I like my students', I know it's not true. All their faces, past, present and future are one. All their parents and all their problems are one. I look around a class of new entrants and eagerly seek the familiar face, the character of ten years ago. He or she is not present, has not been present for years. He or she is a bank manager or a refuse operative with Wansdyke Council, a postperson or one half of a one-parent-family. God forbid, some of them have even become schoolteachers!

I have decided to keep a diary for this reason, then: I feel I'm on a treadmill. Life goes on with little to indicate the passing of years except that my hair thins, the front of the house needs periodical repainting, standards fall on Radio Four, June Knox-Mawer's voice ripens . . . in fact *nothing* happens.

Oh yes yes, I know. This is an orgy of self-doubt brought about by over-indulgence. We are, after all, celebrating the mid-winter fest. Today *is* New Year's Day. Too much turkey and plum pudding, too much James Bond film and Queen's Speech maketh a man unhealthy, fat and miserable.

Even allowing for square eyes and flatulence, though, I am not over-reacting.

The problem is, my interest in cricket is waning! My bowling arm drops year by year. My batting average has never again reached the dizzy heights (over twenty) it did in my twenty-third year. Nowadays I am forced to field in the slips. Should I ever need to return from the boundary I have to bowl or underarm it.

So I have vowed to write this diary, lose a stone and be firm(er) with Elizabeth — my wife. I have determined to get myself fit. I will push my batting average back over ten. More ambitiously, I have sworn to raise the consciousness of the girls on the Pre-Nursing course . . . at the moment this centres (perhaps understandably) on that which is merely physiological.

I have written here resolutions for the New Year, barely begun as that New Year is. We shall see.

2

Sunday 2nd January

I awoke with a sore face and a cramped shoulder. For some deep (and, in the end, unfathomable) reason, Elizabeth can't bear me to sleep with her while her mother's in the house. Our semi is three-bedroomed. One bedroom is a study, one is ours and one for guests. Since 24th December I've been sleeping on a sun-lounger in the study. I have to stay rigidly still while I sleep, otherwise I end up as the filling in a sun-lounger sandwich. I never manage it. The rotten contraption collapses at least twice a night. Last night I gave up and slept on the floor, but it's no good. I roll in my sleep, and twice I found myself jammed between desk and filing cabinet . . . it's amazing the muck that falls into a gap like that.

Meanwhile mother-in-law snores in the guest room, and I can't have a drink because Elizabeth has hidden it all in a stout wooden box under our bed. I must concentrate fiercely on not being rude to the mother. It's not that I dislike her, for she is a perfectly affable example of English, late-middle-aged (very), lower-middle-class (exteremely) womanhood. As long as she can have her hair set every couple of days, as long as she can spend thirty pounds in Marks and Spencer's every Saturday, as long as she can listen to the Archers, and as long as she can eat as much food in a day as an African tribe does in a week, my mother-in-law is happy. The problem is not her. The problem is Elizabeth. As her mother enters the house my wife regresses. She becomes a teenager. 'Oh Mummee!' she'll say as the woman approaches the house. 'Oh Mummee!' as she takes the M & S showerproof mac. 'Oh Mummee! don't sit there, sit here by me!' 'Oh Mummee! What *have* you been doing?' Since I know the conversation that follows off by heart I don't mind lugging Mummee's coat and bag upstairs.

But I do mind when she yells after me, 'Just make us all a nice cup of tea, will you George?' I swear to myself that she can push her daughter about but never me. *Oh no.* I still make the tea of course; well, it seems so unreasonable not to.

I won't be accused of unreasonableness.

Mummee! isn't allowed to know that Elizabeth smokes. Mummee! isn't allowed to know that Elizabeth drinks. We have to hide all alcohol except the Harvey's Bristol Cream (which Mummee! drinks and seems to consider nonalcoholic).

3

For Mummee!'s sake we have to listen to that ghastly Richard Baker on the radio.

'I do *so* like classical music, George. Perhaps we'll listen to Desert Island Discs too.' And she smiles sweetly. Elizabeth and I agree (yes, Mummee!) that we shall listen to Desert Island Discs, but Elizabeth frowns a warning when I offer to throw in Down Your Way, jolly old Johnners and all. 'I do *so* like . . . .' Ugh!

'Desert Island Discs isn't on till next Saturday,' I say, 'so we'll simply have to wait for that.' Elizabeth frowns again, and I get the distinct impression that if I carry on we'll be sleeping in separate rooms long after Mummee!'s gone back to Corsham (where her lair is).

I am not entirely unsympathetic with Elizabeth, I know all about oppressive relationships with mothers. But this is not the time or place to explore that question. Enough personal revelations for today.

*

Mid-morning, Patel called round. What seemed to be an entire fleet of wheezing Toyota and Datsun cars parked outside my house — or rather, outside my house and those of six of my neighbours. Lots of thin Asian boys spilled out of the cars and stood shivering on the edge of my lawn. I could see them from my chair in front of the log-effect fire. What a strange sensation to be warm and cosy in my own front room watching those thin boys gathering on my lawn! The wintry wind flapped their flared, permanent-press trousers. After the excesses of our own Yuletide I felt as if I were observing an army of Bob Cratchits.

'George:' Patel stood on the doorstep with an old bat and ball in his hands, 'My nephews and I thought we'd' see the New Year in 'in the appropriate style.'

'Yes,' I answered slowly, 'but that was yesterday. Today's the second.' I was buttoning-up my clothes, having been caught *déshabille* by Patel's unexpected call. 'You must be mad, Patel. It's freezing.'

'Start the year as you mean to go on, George. Just break up the old Christmas fat, eh? Work off some turkey. You could use it, old chap.' Patel talks as if he's been on a time-capsule from the nineteen thirties. I always expect him to offer a chota-peg or break into a popular song of the period. He's only forty-one, though, and has spent thirty-nine of those years in England. The first two he spent in British East Africa.

'I haven't eaten too much,' I said, straining a shirt button, 'and I'm not coming out. It'll rain soon, look.' I pointed at the sky. The Asian nephews at my lawn's edge looked up too, though they couldn't have heard what I'd said. Dark clouds covered the sky. Patel's bell-bottomed nephews pointed too. I nursed a hope they might restrain Patel, but no such luck.

'Don't be faint-hearted, George old thing. You have to start somewhere . . . anyway, the club bag is in your garage. Come on, chop-chop.'

'No,' I said firmly. The whole idea was crackpot. 'I've got to do some marking.'

Mummee! came into the hallway.

'George,' she said, 'it's absolutely freezing in here, can't you shut the door? I've put some of those nice Marks and Spencer mince pies in the oven and Elizabeth wants to know would you like to . . . .' She stopped and stared at Patel, then at the nephews on the lawn. 'Why are all those blacks standing on our grass?'

That made up my mind. I pulled on my windcheater and fetched the garage key. Patel came to help with the bag.

'Are *all* those boys your nephews?' I asked.

'No.' He shook his head and blinked up at me from behind his thick spectacles. 'Some are my cousins and the one driving the first car is my elder brother, who has come a long long way to be with us at Christmas.'

'Where from?' I asked. A vision of the streets of Delhi floated before me. Or perhaps the brother came from some hilly, far-off place under the shadow of Kilimanjaro. Shafts of sunlight would break through at midday, like a painting by Turner. The brother's mysterious dusky wife would brew herb tea.

'Rugby,' he answered.

I rolled the trusty old Cortina onto the drive. After the kerfuffle that followed ('*Don't* be childish, George, *why* don't you ever think of anyone but yourself. Poor Mummee!'s only here for a few days . . .', etcetera) I couldn't help but think of the Patel clan's patient womenfolk, staying quietly at home, kneading chapatis, cracking spices with rolling pins and talking of loyalty to their lifemates. Ah, if the old ways have virtues, our Asian guests have preserved them.

As the small convoy of rusting Japanese cars followed me out of The Glebe (our street, a cul-de-sac) I couldn't resist looking in my rear-view mirror. *My* womenfolk were standing on the lawn, Elizabeth in a white Pineapple exercise suit, M-in-law in a voluminous pink housecoat with my new cardy over the top. Her fluffy slipper toes peeked over the turf. Her hands were on her hips. There would be no chapatis for *me*. The mince pies would be scoffed or burned by the time *I* returned.

*

As I predicted, when we reached the park the rain was bucketing down. I wanted to sit in the car until it eased, but the Patels (as I suppose one must refer to them *en masse*) would have none of it. We took up station in the centre of a huge, red-cinder soccer pitch and marked out a wicket. Within minutes we had a very jolly single-wicket competition going — rain or no rain. What fun! I soon forgot the weather. All the Patels played well, and had come to enjoy themselves.

As my luck would have it, I had been drawn against one of Patel's cousins, a new arrival from the sub-continent. I padded up, walked to the crease and took a guard. He stood four steps behind the bowling crease, stepped forward and, with the smoothest arm action I have ever seen, fairly whipped the ball down at me. I was ready, or so I thought, and got my foot right forward only to see the wretchedly soaked ball stick on the first bounce and trickle against my toe.

The question was asked and the finger raised. Disaster! Looking back at my wicket I could see they were right . . . but it's so disappointing to start the year in such a fashion. I was angry at myself. I hoped the sub-continental Patel cousin couldn't bat . . . though I really couldn't see myself being able to tweak the ball on this 'wicket'.

I was ten runs down. I must concentrate, I thought. The cousin started forward again, the ball stuck again, though this time I was prepared and managed to dig it out with the toe of my bat. I was still ten down.

The third ball was a full toss which I hooked. It landed a mere twenty feet behind me, towards fine leg. I stared in frank amazement. The cousin had given a quickish delivery, and I'd caught it well on the face of the bat. *Why* didn't it carry? The ball was wet but not *that* wet. My concentration must have broken at this point. At all events I gave my wicket away three times in the next two overs, while scoring only four runs plus four byes. The sub-continental Patel cousin had warmed up a little by now and was bowling off six paces. The four runs came off a snick. The four byes came for a ball which reached me as a full toss: the wicket keeper didn't see it at all and I would swear even this evening as I write that I turned and saw the ball bounce only twice before disappearing into the gloom of the outfield. The Patel cousin was very quick. I had given my wicket away four times and only scored eight. 40 against, 8 for; a debit of 32. The outlook didn't seem good. I could always hope for snow, I mused.

I offered the sub-continental Patel the pads.

'Oh no,' he said, 'I don't think I need pad.'

He didn't. I'm always rusty at the start of the season, but beginning on 2nd January is too much! It took me four balls before I could pitch one on the wicket. Needless to say the cousin ('*I don't think I need pad*' indeed!) despatched this delivery to the boundary with a vigour which belied the sodden condition of ball, players and field. Patel's older brother from Rugby scurried after it, looking for all the world like a Kiplingesque bearer gone for another bottle of gin.

My next ball slipped a mere fifteen feet wide of the wicket. Would this over ever finish? I thought as I plodded wearily back to my mark. I was wet, tired, out of condition . . . thoroughly miserable. The dizzy round of end-of-term parties was obviously taking its toll. Too much rum punch. I looked up the ghastly cinder track to the face of my tormentor. He grinned. The rain fell yet more quickly. I knew that when I did finally get a ball to pitch he was going to thump it as he had the last.

I started forward, bowled. The ball pitched and the sub-continental cousin whacked it on its way. Four more. The ball was returned. I started forward again.

'What do you think you are doing? Are you mad?' A plummy but clearly Asian woman's voice called. 'You will get pneumonia, you fool. Are you mad? What, must I drive you back to Rugby? How can I, you fool, you madman!'

We all turned and looked. The voice came from a small fat Asian woman wearing a black gaberdine mackintosh over a pink chiffon sari. She was carrying an umbrella and she was still shouting. Mrs Rugby Patel (for such she was) had her children around her, all small, all fat and each carrying an umbrella appropriate to his or her size.

Rugby Patel trotted sheepishly towards his family but even so the wife didn't stop. 'In the rain, too. You madman. You fool. I will not be responsible for your health in the rain.' She shook her head for emphasis. 'No. But I will have to feed and clothe my children alone when you are dead from pneumonia in the English rain. *Madman!*' She spat the last word. She looked as if she would box Rugby Patel's ears when she got him home.

Some other Asian women left the shelter of a huge chestnut tree and stood on the sideline yelling too.

The cricket match broke up. All the men (with the exception of my opponent and myself) trotted over to the women. Children milled about, there was a great hubbub. The group edged towards the shelter of the chestnut tree again. In its winter state the tree didn't give much shelter but the Patel clan gathered under it anyway. An impromptu family party seemed to have started.

I feigned bowling at the sub-continental Patel. He smiled and lifted his bat. 'You had me worried,' he said . . . a kindly act, I thought.

'Are you the only bachelor here?' I asked.

'Oh no. I am not bachelor. My wife is beautiful blonde European archaeologist. Very slim, very English, very obedient. Only wants to brush dust off Mogul shards.' There was a twinkle in his eye, I was sure. He rubbed his palm along the face of the old bat Patel had brought. 'Very good cook. Very submissive. English women make good wife.'

I pulled stumps and we splashed together to the boundary. The sub-continental Patel joined a blonde, angular Englishwoman who never allowed her eyes to meet mine. I bade the chattering clan farewell, leaving them to nibble sweetmeats and re-establish diplomatic ties between the sexes. Rain plopped through the branches of the chestnut, but the Patels didn't seem to mind.

I was home by four. Game for a Laugh was on the t.v. One would need to be, I thought. Telly schedules have been re-arranged so that anyone who desires it can watch non-stop light entertainment. Elizabeth sat by her mother's acrylic-shod feet cracking brazil nuts into a bowl.

'We thought you'd eat out so we haven't saved you anything,' she said. 'There's cold turkey or sausage rolls in the fridge.'

I didn't complain. What's the point? I took a sausage roll up to the study and munched it while I knocked-in my new bat (an early Christmas present to myself in November). The knocking-in is done with an old ball inside a sock. Either the bat, the ball or the sock has to be soaked in bat oil, a kind of linseed. Unfortunately, I can never remember which and sometimes get splattered with oil during the first few knocks because I've put it on the wrong bit.

I can't imagine *why* I couldn't get the ball to pitch today. It's so disappointing.

I read three chapters of Buchan's life of Cromwell, then went down to socialize. Elizabeth and Mummee! were watching a James Bond film and 'shushed' me when I tried to raise the subject of the investment of Basingstoke.

'Perhaps we might drive out and visit the ruins of the Basinghouse?' I suggested.

'Shussssh!' all round. I went upstairs again. To the bathroom.

I stripped off and practised my over-arm movement. Nothing wrong with the muscular part but I'm almost *sure* I can hear a little click in my shoulder socket. It's hard to say. I can't swing my arm freely in the bathroom, so I have to kneel and lean to one side to do it. In the silence of the bathroom I also noticed that I give a little grunt as the arm goes over. Perhaps that's why I've never noticed the click before. I'll have to visit the doctor once the holiday is over.

I tried the shoulder a few more times, and noticed that each time it goes over I grunt involuntarily . . . uh, uh, uh! If I swing my arm quickly lots of times I sound like a steam engine . . . whuhuhuhuhush! I will definitely take this to the doctor.

I stopped when there was a knock on the bathroom door.

'I've finished really, I'll just get dressed,' I said.

I thought that was a pretty polite answer, but when I came out my M-in-law glared at me and said, 'Can't you exercise some self-control? At your age too.'

Sometimes I think she's very eccentric. She certainly says some odd things. What self-control is needed in the bathroom? The mind boggles. I said, rather grandly, 'I would have thought self-control would be the sort of thing that stops people watching telly all night.' And stamped off to the study and my sun-lounger to write this diary. I felt *very* superior having taken that off my chest . . . self-control indeed!

Monday 3rd January
Bank Holiday. Lyall kept his head below the parapet. Shoulder is *painful.*

Tuesday 4th January
I awoke with a sore face and a *frozen* shoulder. Mummee! is an insomniac but Elizabeth isn't, so I have to breakfast with M-in-law. Like the sub-continental Patel's wife she won't catch my eye — though there the resemblance ends.

'Are you going to play cricket today, George?' she asked, still without looking at me. It was a trap, I knew. If I said, 'Don't be ridiculous, it's January the fourth,' she'd come back with, 'Well, *that* never bothered you the day before yesterday'.

'No.' I stood. 'I'm going to see the doctor today.'

'Good idea,' Mummee! said (though she still wouldn't look me in the face) and she saw me to the door and helped me on with my coat.

MacPherson, my doctor, is a Boswellian figure with a red face and breath that smells of alcohol at — it seems — any hour of the day. The reason I stick with him is that he hasn't 'modernised' into the system of appointments that everyone else has gone in for. There's nothing more disappointing than to phone the doctor hoping for some sympathy towards your sore throat/broken nose/upset tummy only to be told that it's not convenient for you to be ill now, but would you like an appointment in three weeks? MacP. doesn't have any truck with that rubbish. If you want to see him you have to sit in his waiting-room for a while and then you simply see him. MacP. doesn't have old women occupying his appointment book for weeks ahead with their varicose veins. He doesn't have an appointment book. He doesn't have old men blocking his waiting room with their suspect tubes, either. MacP. keeps his waiting room freezing. I read a Christmas 1964 edition of *Time* magazine for half an hour in this sub-zero hinterland before I saw him.

'Happy Hogmanay the noo, Doctor MacPherson, and how are you?' I enquired.

'I am not here, Mr Lyall, so that people may enquire after *my* health. What can I do for you?' MacP. has no sense of humour to speak of. I indicated the offending joint, took my jacket off and gave him the story.

'And what happens?' he asked.

'If I swing my arm over my head it clicks,' I answered.

'Can't you just not swing your arm over your head?'

'I'm a cricketer.'

His eyes appeared to glaze over. Shades of 'England, their England', I thought. MacP. is clearly not a kindred spirit. He looked at his watch and said testily, 'Show me then.'

I swung the arm.

'Uh.'

'Why do you make that noise?' MacP. asked.

'I don't know. It's an automatism.'

'How can it be an automatism? Do it again.'

I swung my arm three times vigorously.

'Uh, uh, uh . . . well?'

'Does it hurt?' he asked.

'It clicks,' I said, 'Couldn't you refer me to a sports clinic?' I'd heard about those on Medicine Now on the BBC.

'What the hell's that?' said MacP.

'A place where sportsmen get treated?' I offered . . . physician heal thyself: why should *I* know better than he?

11

'All that stuff's private. Do you want to go private?'

You could almost hear the rustle of pound notes as he said 'private'. Just like a dentist . . . . 'I'll have to pull that one out.' 'Can't you cap it?' 'Not on the NHS, I'm afraid.' 'How much would it cost?' '*Nurse*! I see Mr Lyall has only one cushion. Bring him another and then kiss his feet for ten minutes while I prepare an estimate.'

I know all about private medicine. I settled for a letter to the NHS bones hospital in Bath and tramped home. M-in-law appears to have become solicitous for my health and asked, 'How did it go?'

'Not badly,' I said.

'And was the doctor able to help with your . . . problem?'

'After a fashion. He's given me a letter to a hospital dedicated to the matter in Bath. He reckons they'll give me a course of whacking great injections right up the middle of it, and says that'll cure the problem in no time at all.'

She shrieked and ran upstairs to Elizabeth. I'd never associated her with squeamishness, I must say.

*

I'm very disappointed about the cricket. After the old year being seen out (if not off) by one of the most exciting matches ever, I desperately wanted to hear the Fifth Test on the radio. I can't, though. Radio Three medium-wave reception is indifferent hereabouts due to the proximity of the Quantocks . . . or is it the Mendips? One of them, anyway, causes problems with the transmitter. I suppose it all hinges on where the transmitter is — Wookey Hole if the bureaucrats had been left to decide it! The World Service, meanwhile, has been adjusted so that we English — who after all are only footing the bill — can't get it very well. A smug man came on Radio Four and explained it all. 'It's all to do with footprints,' he said. Bureaucrat boot-prints, more like! Iron-heel prints!

So, shorn of both Radio Three and the World Service on the medium-wave band I was forced to resort to the short wave band . . . chasing up and down it looking for bulletins like some poverty-stricken African seeking news from the mother country. The bushman's truth emanates from the few surviving pink bits on the map. Bush House is the conduit. I am a West Country bushman . . . if I'm lucky.

At 2 a.m. I gave up. After all, college starts back tomorrow and I must be alert.

Earlier, I had been gratified to learn (when I strolled down to The Dog and Bucket to watch recorded highlights of last night's play on t.v. in their saloon bar) that ours had not been the only cricket match spoiled yesterday . . . but at least ours was spoiled only by the rain. What about Dyson's run-out? An Englishman would have walked, I'm sure . . . but what can you expect of the Antipodeans with their revolting cartoon duck, 'tinnies' and win-at-all-costs attitude? The umpire claimed Dyson was 'six inches in or six inches out' and so gave the benefit of the doubt. One wonders to which other areas of life Australians would like to apply this truly 'new math'? Qantas flights destined for London would suddenly start disgorging their beer-swilling passengers onto the unsuspecting burghers of Lugano. 'G' day sport! This Earls Court?'

When I came home from The Dog and Bucket M-in-law and E. were watching t.v. They had found a game-show which required all the brain cells of a lobotomised ant. Elizabeth toasts muffins while her mother sits glued to the box. I retired to the fugitive delights of the World Service. Has Botham held the catch? Who knows?' *This wavelength will be broadcasting our Spanish service for the next hour.* Will Arkle bat tonight (or today, in Australia)? He has replaced Fowler, hit on the toe in Melbourne . . . many may think this a lucky and honourable let-out for selectors. I try the medium wave again. Got it loud and clear on Radio Three! Then a Spaniard breaks in again. Is this a Latin plot? I dash up the dial to World Service medium-wave, tune in for long enough to hear, 'And what do you think of . . . ?' before I find myself listening to a *French* game-show. Are the French so addicted to game-shows that they'll listen to them at what must be 2.45 a.m. their time? Perhaps Elizabeth's mother should move there.

By 2.00 a.m. Greenwich Mean Time (we don't mess around with foreign time *here*) I have no time to spare. I'm extremely tired and must snuggle up on the sun-lounger. I am very careful not to lie on my right (i.e. clicking) shoulder.

Wednesday 12th January (8 days later)

Deep snow over England. People wishing to brown their knees can't get out of Gatwick. People wishing to come in (having browned theirs) are forced to sit and simmer in foreign parts, sipping their filthy Pina Coladas and eating steak tough enough to mend boots with. Hard cheese on them!

Meanwhile back in England we faithful crewmen of the good ship Albion dubbin our street shoes, slip patented anti-skidding devices onto our soles, wrap up well and crunch down the salted pathways of Mugsborough. Loyal to the last, we educators stick to our task.

I saw an advert today in the travel agents for 'cricket holidays' in Malaga. Or was it Majorca? Or Malibu? I could take the time off work (heaven knows, I haven't been sick in years!) but I'm just not match fit. Nor are my injections up to date.

I stayed up (talking of holidays) and watched highlights of the pyjama cricket in Australia. 'Highlights' is perhaps too strong a word. Australia batted badly, England worse. Players complained about being blinded by the floodlights — one presumes they've introduced a sunshade-wallah from Delhi to help the poor darlings deal with daytime cricket! The only people who had a good day were the fancy-dress designers, the white ball manufacturers and a certain Mr Extras, who was outscored by only three players on the Australian side and one (Lamb) on the English. In fact, considering Lamb is South African (but I won't go into all that now), the highest scoring *English* Englishman was Botham, who scored eighteen.

I'm beginning to believe that this tour has not been an unqualified success. Perhaps I should write to HQ, pointing out I've a new bat, have broken in my 'Sunil Gavaskar' boots and am available to tour.

I wonder if anyone has told 'Bob Dylan' Willis that his pop star hero's real name is Zimmerman? Perhaps he'll have to change his initials again to R.D. (Z). Willis. How could such an accident-prone man be put in charge of England?

February — Rugger persons rule the roost at Hacks' Ground. We will have to make our wicket where the scrum is!

Tuesday 8th February

A Tuesday evening. I hate the winter and February is definitely not spring. A freezing, pitch-dark evening with rain seeming to curve just as it's about to hit the earth, deciding instead to hurl itself against my new *Patio Window Welkomwarm Wonderglass. P3W*, as the salesman called it, the revolutionary new system which will halve your heating bills *immediately*. He put a lot of stress on that *immediately*. I wonder. I'm sure I can see a trickle by the edge at the bottom. Elizabeth says it's condensation and dabs her brow with a small crushed handkerchief to indicate she feels the room is stuffy. We've practised the room-temperature-argument many times and we never get a result. Nowadays when my wife dabs her brow I simply affect not to notice.

These windows cost five hundred pounds! It's very testing that they leak . . . I'm sure standards of craftsmanship are dropping. I'm sure that, should I be brave enough to bring the fault to the attention of the *Patio Window Wonderwarm*

15

Welkglase representative, I will only be met with insolence. If they leak and leak and leak and leak *Patio Wonderwind* ... oh, *P3W* (now I know the reason for the acronym) will simply send some unskilled operative to smear the cheapest putty on the offending part.

*

I haven't been very good about keeping my diary, I know. January has slipped by with barely a comment from yours truly. I have excuses, but I still feel I have broken my word to myself. I will definitely write *every day* from now on.

I've been very good about 'netting', though. Throughout December Patel and I netted in the sports centre . . . irregularly, I'll admit; but every little helps. Because of 'club bookings' we've been forced off to a great extent in January (in truth we've only managed two 'nets') but the spirit is willing, and I am confident as we approach the new season. Tonight is Old Hackham's CC AGM and I believe Patel and myself are two members at least who can approach the meeting with a clear conscience about our commitment to club and game. I have even taken an extremely painful course of injections in my right shoulder, which was clicking and sometimes even freezing-up during December and January. There's dedication for you! I'm only brought on as fifth-change bowler to trundle a few while the good bowlers have a rest, but I still see the need to keep myself in peak physical condition . . . for cricket, that is. I'm not a gymnast. Actually the injections were administered by a certain Doctor Drax, who was about twenty-seven, wore the most heavenly perfume and leaned over me oozing gorgeousness as she injected me. All this on the national health!

When I mentioned Dr Drax to Elizabeth she scowled and suggested I . . . well, I'm not writing what she suggested here. I just wish such thoughts were not in her. Contact with the Bristol teaching fraternity seems to have coarsened my wife. Too much inner-city social realism, *I* know.

16

I noticed that the Principal's Sec. has swapped from ordinals to cardinals when representing dates on official letters. So will I . . . if it's good enough for Enid (the secretary), it's good enough for me.

Yesterday, 8 Feb (there, I've the hang of it already) was something of a red-letter day for me. I was voted secretary of OHCC.

I will explain for the benefit of a future historian who may chance on this work. I was born in Mugsborough. I went to the local grammar, Hackham's GS. Hackham owned a foundry which supplied railings to the big cities in the area — i.e. Bath and Bristol — during the eighteenth-century building boom. To make up for a lifetime of ill-treating his workers, stealing from his clients and impregnating half the women in Somerset, Hackham built six narrow and unhygienic almshouses in Mugsborough and endowed the local school with a couple of thousand pounds. Hence *Hackham's* GS; though by the same logic it should have been known as Macmillan's GS when I went there. Macmillan's government was, after all, putting up the cash. Hackham's name was carved over the portals, though, and stamped inside the library books. Hackham's life story was on the lips of every twelve-year-old who crossed the threshold. It must be the best two thousand pounds Hackham ever spent.

After university I came back to teach in Mugsborough at what was now Hackham's Co-educational Comprehensive. I immediately began playing cricket for OHCC and have considered myself a stalwart ever since. The trouble is now that Hackham's Co-educational Comprehensive has been merged with two other comprehensive schools to form Mugsborough Comp., a huge place with thousands of students and a complex of buildings built atop what was once Grange Farm. The sixth-form was merged with several others to become Mugsborough College, at which I am now a lecturer in History and Brit. Con. To put the matter concisely, there are no more Old Hackhamians to be had. The supply has dried up.

At one time we considered changing our name to

'Mugsborough Schools Old Boys CC' so making younger people feel eligible, but word came (via the OB Association) that Old Hackham's RFC, our sister organization, was agin the move. It seems they felt that yelling 'Come on you Mugs!' from the touchline didn't have quite the same ring to it as 'Come on you Hacks!' I can't say as I blamed them, and nor did anyone else . . . so 'Old Hack's' it has stayed.

*

The AGM can be a pathetic business. We field only one side and call on upwards of forty playing members plus maybe half a dozen casuals in the course of the season. We have some thirty or so honorary vice-presidents, plus Albert. You'd think the meeting would be well attended. It wasn't. I caught the bus into town (these aren't, after all, teetee meetings) and strolled into the saloon bar of The King Henry's Goose with five minutes to spare before the meeting should begin. Not a sausage. The bar was empty . . . . I couldn't even rouse the barman. I went round to the public. Nothing. I went up the narrow stairway to our hired room. It was deserted, no welcoming fug and clinking glasses, no 'Hail George, well met'; nothing. I began to worry. Perhaps I'd come on the wrong night. I checked my diary. It was the right night. . . . Besides, there was the business of the missing barman. Perhaps everyone else had some information denied to me — a brief message from the Russians? — and had rushed off to spend their last 3¾ minutes with their loved ones. I looked out onto the street. Buses passed, strollers strolled (if any form of perambulation could be described as 'strolling' on a wet February night), the shoplights flickered. Whatever had turned The Goose into a dry-land Marie Celeste, my fellow Mugsborians were as yet as ignorant as myself. It was a mystery.

I helped myself to a half-pint of dry cider and slouched unhappily on a bar stool. Suddenly I heard a voice.

'Fnuh fnuh fnuhfnh.'

I followed the sound. It was a muffled voice, a man's voice.

'Oh, come *on*!' Another voice.

'*Fnuh* fnuhfnuh.'

It was *two* voices. It was two men's voices . . . and they

seemed to come from The Goose's cellar. The voices rose, as it were, beneath my very feet.

'Well I don' fnuhfnuhfnuh.'

I ventured behind the bar. The voices seemed louder. I opened the door to the cellar. They seemed louder yet. I descended into the gloom. In the shafts of light that fell from the bar-room I saw what appeared to be a rugby scrimmage at the foot of the stairs.

'*Come on* Albert, sort yourself out.'

'Yer silly old sod.'

I heard the last sentence most distinctly. It was the barman. I could hear other voices, muttering. Then curses, then 'ows' and 'ouches', 'did you have to stand there you silly oaf', and sundry other expressions of vehemence. Then, as if a chorus, they all said, 'Don't shut the door!'

Somehow I managed to talk them out. I felt as a senior policeman might when he deals with a hijack or as a priest might when he winkles the broken bottle from his distraught parishioner's hand. I felt *heroic*.

'Look here, you lot, what's going on?' I said.

Retrospectively, I suppose my greatest feat was to keep Albert out of the barman's hands. 'Murder in King Henry's Goose' would not have looked good as a headline in the *Mugsborough Evening Chronicle*. I bought the would-be murderer and the would-be murderee a Guinness each and sent Albert up to the hired room.

Before I tell the story, I need to write about Albert. Albert has been connected with Hackham's GS longer than any other man living. When I went there he was the second history master. The first was a man called Spaight who had a residual cockney accent and called himself (to our ears) 'Spite'. It was well suited. Spite had his own room, in one corner of which he had built stacks of books, piles of correspondence, heaps of old exam papers and odd pieces of pre-WWII grammar school memorabilia into what might only be fairly described as a 'lean-to'. Spite hid in his lean-to, shellacking old cricket balls so that they could be re-used, learnings old *Wisdens* off by heart. Occasionally he would send Albert out of the lean-to and Albert would be expected to hand out books, give and collect homework, and, most important of all, maintain discipline. Spite only surfaced from April on. We learned History by osmosis. I always thought of Albert as Spite's younger assistant, so you may imagine my surprise when I returned from university to find that Albert had retired and Spite was Head of Department . . . now he had a *real* office to hide in. In time I took over the lean-to; funnily enough, I have never pulled it down.

On retirement Albert took over responsibility for OHCC, and he is now our Honorary Mr President. Far from being Spite's younger assistant, Albert was in his sixties while Spite was a mere stripling of forty-odd. Albert has gone to OHCC while Spite is even today my HOD. Spite is a general, Albert a soldier. Albert means well, he just never does very well. Although he's never been a player, he's regularly attended OHCC matches for many years. At one time we made him scorer (umpire was out of the question, though even now he offers) but he couldn't keep up. His pencil always broke and then he'd be scurrying round for one while two more wickets fell. It was more than an umpire dared do to lose count while Albert was scoring.

(Umpire) 'How many Albert?'

(Albert) 'How many what?'

(Umpire) 'How many balls?'

(Albert) 'What?'

(Umpire) 'Balls!'

Then Albert would get in a huff and there would follow a brief discussion between the captains. Three more balls would be played, whether we had already had one or five.

No. Albert was no good as a scorer. We made him fixtures secretary. Our captain at the time (another George like myself) made all the arrangements. All Albert had to do was make a note of the fixtures, then cough up the information on the appropriate day to the match committee. Albert lost the book. We put him in charge of the provision of match balls, All he did was buy a gross of Indian quarter balls which lost all their bounce on the second over and turned so viciously that we ended up playing a second innings each in a match which only lasted from mid-day to sunset on a summer's Sunday. I can't give the scores . . . the leaves were discreetly torn from the score books and both teams sworn to silence. We still have 139 Indian quarter balls and they're so dangerous we don't even use them for nets. When I offered them at a vast discount to the PE wallah at Mugsborough Comp. he just laughed haughtily and strode away. Now the Indian quarter balls are in Albert's loft and we have entrusted the purchase of equipment to a committee.

When I went into the cellar of The King Henry's Goose Albert was at the bottom of the scrimmage. The other members were OHCC players, a laundry delivery man and the aforesaid barman of the aforesaid pub.

The barman was new. It seems that Albert had come in, ordered a Guinness and introduced himself as the President of Old Hackham's Cricket Club. He'd demanded the key to the hired room. The barman couldn't help. He went down to the cellar, came back and told Albert that, though the keys were kept in the cellar entrance, none seemed appropriate for the hired room. Albert offered to help. The barman will know better next time. They both went into the cellar.

'Be careful with the latch,' said the barman.

'What latch?' said Albert, standing in the entrance.

Click.

The door shut.

The next thing was that they lost the light switch (not surprising, this, as it's on the stairway). They stumbled around in the gloom, then took to yelling for help. Albert is a good yeller, in fact I can hardly think of one better. But he usually takes his teeth out first. On this occasion Albert left his teeth where they were and yelled.

The barman yelled, 'Help!'

Albert yelled, 'Help!'

The barman yelled, 'Help!'

Albert yelled, 'Hilf!'

The barman said, 'Are you German?'

'Sherman?' said Albert. 'Ahf thought in thwo world wrsh tho that the like of Hugh could be free. Don't accush *me* of being a Sherman.' A slight exaggeration — even Albert isn't old enough to have fought in both wars.

The barman claims Albert lunged at him next, Albert says he tripped in the dark. One way and another, Rudi Brathweight, our West Indian fast bowler came downstairs and found them in each other's arms, each claiming to be looking for Albert's teeth.

Rudi laughed.

'Don' lesh the door closhe!' cried Albert.

'What?' said Rudi.

Click.

The door closed.

A similar scene had been played out with several more Old Hacks, each come early to The Goose and each attracted by the noise. Even our vice-captain Paul Peterson (Albert had him in the score book as Peter Paulson, of course), a smartypants if ever there was one and a regular scorer of fifties, had fallen in with them. It seems there *are* some situations in which a seat on the board of your father's insurance brokerage and the ownership of a new BMW can't help . . . or so Peterson discovered. I enjoyed releasing him.

The laundry delivery man refused to give any account of himself, simply slouching up the stairs and leaving in a sulk.

Rudi had drunk more than one Carlsberg Special during their confinement. He also produced fresh bottles from his pockets at intervals throughout the rest of the evening.

Peterson had to rush back to his BMW, ostensibly to fetch his pocket calculator, but I believe he went for a comb — such is his vanity.

I had to buy the barman *two* Guinnesses. And then we couldn't find the key to the hired room.

*

'I wants to ree-co-mend George as our secretary,' said Rudi. It was after half past nine and we were still dishing out jobs for the new season. I mustn't say the honour was entirely unexpected . . . that would be an untruth. I have been temporary secretary ever since Coggins, our last Hon. Sec. was caught . . . well, I don't want to go into that. Why write unsavoury things in your diary? And certainly Coggins won't see these pages. He'll have plenty of hours for contemplation as he paces his cell. No, I won't mention Coggins' heinous crimes.

'Seconder?' said Albert.

There was one, George Jolly, our former captain. I was installed without a vote. It's a strange thing, but I was quite moved . . . after all, I've now been involved with OHCC for fifteen years and this is my first big official job.

I only wish the rest of the meeting had passed so smoothly.

First there was the business of the quorum. Biggs (a slow left-armer who does nothing with the ball but keeps it hanging in the air for so long that all but the most patient batsmen eventually madden and toss their bats at it like so many whirling dervishes) has recently been elected Mother-of-Chapel or whatever the equivalent Trade Union rank is when applied to a bank. Having failed, in his mid-thirties, to become a big cheese in the bank Biggs has set his sights on becoming a big cheese in the bank's union (or rather not-the-bank's-union). Biggs toiled for fifteen years behind his mahogany counter before discovering he was working-class. The experience has distressed him — even addled his brain a little. He now affects a northern accent and reads (as much as anyone can be said to) the *Sun* newspaper.

When our AGM opened properly Biggs — who now considers himself an expert in these matters — told us we needed a quorum before we could open the meeting. Once we had a quorum we could open the meeting and then have a *proper* vote on whether I should be Hon. Sec.

'But we've had a proper vote,' said Albert, waggling his pencil in a chairmanly manner.

'Not without a quorum, you haven't, Mr Chair.'

Albert ignored the fact that Biggs, a former pupil of his, appeared to have forgotten his name and asked, patiently, 'How do you propose we get a quorum?'

'You hold a vote at the meeting to decide how many your quorum should be, then that's it . . . that's your number. As long as you've got that number, your meeting is quorate. You have a quorum.' Biggs sat back in his chair and folded his arms. To a great brain like his it was such a simple matter.

'But,' persisted Albert Chair, 'didn't you say we needed a quorum *before* we could hold the meeting?'

'Yes, of course!' snapped Biggs. We were all so slow.

'Then how can we have a meeting to decide the quorum if we haven't already got a quorum?'

Biggs face was blank for a second. I imagined him making up some double-entry ledger for the logic. Whatever else banks teach their employees, set theory doesn't figure in the clerk's syllabus.

Suddenly Biggs' expression became fierce.

'Our meeting is *inquorate*!' he exclaimed.

George, our former captain, saved the evening from being completely wasted in this fashion by quickly proposing Biggs for Club Treasurer (a job Coggins had combined with that of Hon. Sec. Given what had happened to *him* . . . well, I'm not going into all that. Let's just say Biggs would do well to count club funds very carefully before assuming responsibility for them). Rudi seconded George's motion — not because he agreed, he told me later, but because George had seconded *his* — and we made Biggs' first job as Club Treasurer the collection of a 'whip', then sent him downstairs for a round of drinks.

While Biggs was out of the way we settled on a quorum of five, voted me in, voted him in and, by the time he was back, were receiving the Captain's Report.

Our captain, Brian Cook, had sent his apologies. It seems he has sprained his back while browning his knees in Tenerife and has been ordered complete bed rest.

'How did he sprain it?' someone asked.

'Pumping up a lilo,' came the reply.

Laughter.

'Is 'lilo' Spanish for a girl?' asked Rudi.

Ribald laughter.

'Come on gentlemen, let's have order,' said Albert, 'we're wasting time.'

What's it to us if Brian Cook contrives to invalid himself in the sunshine (knowing Brian, he couldn't be *moved*, of course) while the rest of us slog it out in the long English winter? Lucky swine! He's self-employed, a general builder and carries umpteen sickness insurances which he invariably calls on during the slack (for his trade) winter period. During the summer, Brian Cook would go in to bat with both arms in plaster and his leg in a splint . . . but come October and the slightest snuffle turns him into a stretcher case. Spraining his back in Tenerife must count as his biggest coup yet. I could foresee the ringing of the Lutine Bell, mass bankruptcy, and a not inconsiderable number of suicides when the news hits Lloyds.

The vice-captain, Paul Peterson, delivered Cooky's report. Peterson is young, blond, rich, well-muscled, good mannered . . . a confident man. Peterson is revolting. He wears pullovers with little crocodiles on the front. Since most of the Captain's Report was about Peterson himself (top of the batting averages, most runs scored in a season, first — and last — to 1,000 runs in the year, most runs scored in a match, most catches held) he had a pretty smug half-hour.

'Thank God the little blighter can't bowl, eh George?' muttered George, our former captain. He was right too — it was insufferable. Not only did we have to listen to Peterson's praises being sung in Peterson's own voice, we then had to listen to a good ticking-off from Brian Cook as to why the rest of us were lazy slackers unworthy of Peterson's company *also* delivered in Peterson's own voice.

A brief respite was had when Patel came in late. His computer had 'gone down'. He'd had to 'stay on', 'help out'. He might be 'called out' again. Why is it that verbs can't do things on their own any more? In modern English, which Patel uses when speaking of his beloved computer, they seem to spend all their time 'huddled up' against prepositions.

Under the circumstances, Patel wanted to know, would we let him put in his two ha'porth there and then? We agreed. Patel formally apologised for his lateness, then treated us to a fifteen-minute eulogy on Paul Peterson. I began to wonder if it was the computer or Patel that had 'gone down'.

Peterson rose, smugger than ever, to remind some of us of our individual failings — thereby concluding the Captain's Report. The Report was unanimously accepted, though I for one was coerced only by my own good manners into saying nothing.

Then Peterson passed round a postcard with a bikini-clad girl on the front and the message, '*I, Brian Cook, hereby resign the captaincy of OHCC*' scrawled on the back. The card smelled of cheap Spanish perfume and I gained the impression that Cooky had sprained his wrist rather than his back — or had he been drinking? The writing was wobbly, anyway. Albert took the card, turning it round and round and looking at it from every conceivable angle . . . as if the card itself were the problem.

'This is very strange, very strange. What should we do about this?' he asked no one and everyone.

We all shook our heads.

Peterson sat puffed up like a sergeant-major. He thought the job was his for the taking. Even his admirers, I'm sure, didn't want Peterson for captain. *I* would hate it. Various hats were thrown into the ring. Everyone avoided Peterson's eyes. Eventually I suggested we put the whole thing off until the season was actually about to start. We could decide at the Practice Match. Meanwhile, Cooky would change his mind. He was probably depressed about being sick. In the Canaries. In the sun. With only girls and brandy for company. Poor old Brian, I said, let's give him a chance to think things over. I'll write back and tell him how we feel. He's best choice for captain anyway. Make up his mind when he comes home.

'What about in between?' asked Peterson, 'we'll need a locum, someone to deal with the Conference, arrange fixtures, that sort of thing.'

I could see his drift. Peterson thought, as vice-capt., he would be the natural choice.

'George Jolly'll do it,' I said, meaning George our former captain, 'he won't have to be a playing captain.'

George agreed, as long as he wasn't expected to play. The matter was formally put to the meeting and passed. I was as glad as anyone to have an experienced man in the job, but I sincerely hope George Jolly *doesn't* have to play as captain — he's too old. George has been 'touching fifty' for all the years I've known him. His fiftieth year has had more touches than a girl in Soho. If George Jolly starts to play regularly again he'll *definitely* have to field in the slips. Old Hacks might find itself starting the season as the only team (outside of the West Indian tourists) to field with two leg slips, three slips, a fly slip and two gullies. With Biggs bowling slow left-armers we would make a pretty sight!

The next item was the tour. Patel has been Tour Captain for the past three seasons. He doesn't like Worthing (where we tour) and he thinks English boarding houses which only provide bacon breakfasts are racialist. Patel has found a nice little touring circuit in the West Midlands and spent all last year trying to talk the rest of us into it. We will not have it. We like our seaside. Patel, meanwhile, refuses to book us in again at the Seaview Conference Centre (actually it's a boarding house with a very large back room and a bar). Patel says he would rather stay in a tent. Some members agree the

Seaview Conference Centre is indeed a dump; however, the proprietress, a certain Mrs Wiggins, offers us very advantageous group rates. George Jolly, in particular, appears to receive facilities from Mrs Wiggins which I can only presume — judging by the way he splashes on aftershave — that his own Mrs Jolly has long since ceased to offer. I am neutral on the matter of touring. I do care, of course, about forcing Patel to play cricket as yet unbreakfasted, but the idea of feasting on halal lamb in Darlaston before slogging it out with railwaymen on some public memorial ground doesn't do much for *me*, either.

Albert, who not only doesn't play and has never toured but also (as far as I can make out) has never set foot in Sussex, gave out at great length on the matter; examining all the possibilities as a President should; listing and weighing pros and cons. Biggs, who also doesn't tour, helped him. Biggs was all for drawing up a set of 'Touring Rules' there and then. We could amend these rules, adding to them, adjusting them at our leisure in a series of motions and votes at regular club meetings.

'I thought the point of having club meetings was to play cricket at them. We meet twice a week from May to September,' said Peterson. I had to agree with him.

'Well,' said Patel, 'I'm not staying in *that* hotel and *that's that!*' I wanted to let the matter drop. We'd resolve it nearer the time. Patel muttered about quotes for marquee hire . . . but I knew I could talk him round.

We ended the evening with a long (and eventually fruitless) discussion about match fees. The barman came up before we were done and did what I can only describe as looking at his watch loudly. It seems he'd been left in sole charge of The King Henry's Goose for the first time tonight and he was determined that the place would be shipshape when the landlord returned (no doubt in the early hours) from his Masonic Lodge meeting in Bristol.

Albert, Patel and myself walked toward the bus station. We'd travelled less than a hundred yards when we were disturbed by the barman running behind us and shouting, 'Mr Patel! Mr Patel! Mr Patel!'

What a kind man! He'd run after us to say that the council had 'phoned up' and that their computer had 'gone down' again. Could Patel possibly 'come round' at this very moment?

The street was empty and the rain was falling and the barman panted as he spoke. We could see the lights of The Goose. Patel thanked the barman profusely. The wind began to gust about us.

Albert pointed at the pub and said, 'Did you bring a key?'

'What?' said the barman.

The wind gusted again and I heard a distant but distinct 'click' as the door closed.

Patel and I simply ran away. Albert hobbled after us as fast as he could.

*

11 p.m. When I reached home Elizabeth was in bed. She says she is unwell. I hope her teaching isn't getting on top of her again. I went downstairs to make some tea and found a little puddle by the *P3W* windows. Condensation, my foot! I will take this up in the morning with the directors of the company that sold them to me.

Tuesday 15 February
Rain.

So much rain has fallen. It hasn't let up since Jan 1, yet still I know that come July 1 squads of blue-serged inspectors from the water board will be roaming the streets of Mugsborough in search of water wastage. Men whose only crime is to swab down the dusty windscreen of their Austin Metros with a dampened sponge will be in danger of forfeiting their freedom. Anyone caught slipping his geraniums an eggcupful of the soft stuff will get six months. We English will become furtive carriers of water by night. Such are the perils of nationalisation. For now it's all the sewers can do to cope with the stuff — and my new windows aren't coping at all.

I have called the Patio Window Wonderglaze Welko people twice a day all week. I always get their answering machine. I suppose the only way to get an answer from a human is to go

to their office. Unfortunately that means more time off work
— and having had three mornings off for shoulder injections
I don't think I can take it. Elizabeth doesn't understand. She
thinks I don't want the windows fixed . . . or so she tells me.

Maybe I could cancel my British Constitution class. I'd
like to. I hate Brit. Con. During today's class the 1st year saw
fit to argue over the pronunciation of Coke. They said, 'How
do you *know* to pronounce it "Cook"?' I said, 'I just know. It's
traditional. Like the Battle of Maldon.' They asked how else
would I have them pronounce Maldon. (I must say I was
surprised they'd heard of it . . . speaks volumes for their
comprehensive school masters, that.) I said, 'It's traditional.
Well known. Conventional, even.'

1st year Brit. Con. looked unconvinced. Show us, they
said. So I did.

A quick scurry round the staffroom, and I came up with a
dog-eared copy of *Sweet's Anglo-Saxon Primer*. When I went
back into the history room I left the door ajar — a mistake I
will not repeat.

I did twenty lines of *The Battle of Maldon* in my best old
English. It sounded, I know, like a Hull trawlerman reciting
from a German phrasebook.

'Gehyrst þu, saelida, hwaet þis folc segeð . . .'

The door behind me creaked and I heard a voice say, '. . .
and Mr Lyall here is teaching British Constitution.'

The sentence was spoken by Channel, our Principal. I
must say the class was amused. Channel (or Coco, as he is
known behind his back), was not visibly amused. He didn't
say anything else. Coco didn't look angry. Coco didn't even
scowl. He just withdrew.

The VIPs followed him, looking puzzled. One man
scratched his head and said to his Tory lady companion,
'What's British Constitution?'

I know how he felt.

The class left my room no nearer achieving their Brit.
Con. 'A'-level than when they came in. My heart isn't in it.
Their (collective) heart isn't in it. I'd much rather talk about
Burke and Tom Paine than the distinction between Privy
Seal, Lord Chancellor, Master of the Rolls — name here any
officer of the crown. All the modern ones are Gilbert and
Sullivan players *manqués*, I know. Precise study of their roles

will lead the students into an intimate knowledge of the rules of a game no one is playing any more. The information I impart will make the students the political equivalent of underarm bowlers. So much for Brit. Con. 'A'-level.

'Coco' Channel will exact retribution for today. He does not like to be embarrassed. He will have his pound of flesh. I was much exercised by this knowledge. Perhaps he'll get Spite to carpet me.

I have two of Albert's Indian quarter balls in my desk. When the Brit. Con. class left I thought I might re-shellac them, much like the Spite of old. It is an art, I now know, calculated to soothe the out-of-season player rather than prepare the balls to be passed off as new on to the unsuspecting captains of sides we travel to. Re-shellacking is like knocking-in bats or polishing bails or reading Robin Marlar — each is an act which pleases the doer not so much by what it means as by the fact that he is doing something connected (more or less) with the summer sport.

*

Spite's a *strange* man. He has four years before he retires and he seems intent on spending those years locked in his office. He ventures out only to meet with Coco and the other HODs, communicating the results of these meetings to us by means of notes pinned to the bulletin board. No one has seen Spite pin up his notices — but they are there. A fresh one (sometimes two) appears every day.

Spite played cricket once. He was very keen. During his earlier days at Hackham's he wasn't qualified to play for OH's (teaching wasn't a qualification in that period; only being an actual old boy would do). Spite played instead for a fairly up-market village team, Netherpopham CC. Rumour has it he wielded the willow well. I wouldn't know about that. Though he coached the school team he never deigned to *demonstrate* anything. Oh no. The coaching I received from Spite came in sentence-sized aphorisms: 'Dropped catches lose matches, Lyall', or 'Good knock, now you've got to field even better'. In my last summer there as a student he said, 'You'll never do it until you get your leg over to the line. You'll learn all about leg-over at university', which, by

Spite's standards, was comparable to the Gettysburg Address. The inference in the second part was clear and, I can admit now in the privacy of this diary, proved false. It's sad to relate but a fact, I'm afraid to say, that even today I play off my back foot too much.

During all this time I've known him, first as his student and now as his underling, Spite has confined himself to few words. Except on one occasion. During my second year of teaching Spite's wife left him. The departure of his posh wife (it was surely *her* money that bought their fine house in Netherpopham) remained unmentioned except as a scandalous rumour for weeks until one day he turned on me in the staffroom and said in a loud voice, 'Did you know my wife's b . . . . . . d off, Lyall?'

'Mm,' I said. Until that moment I hadn't realised floorboards could be so interesting.

'Seems some gardener bloke was rogering her while I was here, administering to the educational needy. My neighbour Colonel 'Blabbermouth' Walker caught them bang to rights in the Rhododendron Dell. Seems the whole village knew before *I* did.'

Miss Trimble, who teaches Home Management (really a Creative Arts subject but she likes to take her tea with us) made a little gurgling noise in her throat, bolted her digestive biscuit and was off in a flurry of tweed skirts and dropped knitting patterns. She has never looked me full in the face since.

'Rogered under my very nose,' said Spite, as loud as ever.

My colleagues were no good. They wouldn't look up. They wouldn't speak. They just slurped tea. *I* had to brazen Spite out alone.

'Mm, Spaight,' I said. 'Hard lines. Tough on you.'

'Rogered by a gardener,' he said.

'Mm, the gardener,' I said.

'Not *our* gardener, of course,' he said.

'No, of *course*,' I said, 'not *yours*.' What a fool I can be! Spite looked at me as if I were barmy, then said, 'No. Not *our* gardener. *He* couldn't raise a gallop. Too old, you see. No one would drop their knickers for him. No point. It was *another* gardener but in *our* Rhododendron Dell.'

'Oh,' I said, 'who?' I swear it was not this brain which

ordered the last word be spoken. It just popped out. Spite wilted, seemed visibly strained.

'*The Nicholls man,*' he said, 'Netherpopham CC's grounds-man chap. Self-employed digger of gardens in the village. While we were paying him to roll our square he was actually rolling my Madeleine. What d'yer think of that, Lyall?'

'Bad business,' I said. People were making excuses to leave the staffroom. Spite held my elbow in a grip of iron.

'Rotten business,' he growled, 'our quickie has had no help from the track all season because that slacker wasn't doing his job. *That's* what made us suspicious.' He whirled and slammed his fist on the staffroom table top, shaking the crockery.

'We lost four matches on the trot. The track was like some bloody *wadi*. The creases are like dustbowls and rain lies in the middle of the square as if it were the village pond. I'm surprised the ducks haven't moved in.'

'Too bad, Spaight,' I said. I looked round for a way out. I couldn't claim I had a class — Spite *knew* I was free next period — but I didn't want the conversation to go on. How could I escape? I felt sorry for Spite. His blue eyes seemed pale and watery with grief. My heart went out to poor gruff Spite. Mere words could not help his anguish.

'It's disgusting,' he said, '. . . *disgusting*. The outfield is so slow you can't score a four. The track's so lumpy you have to watch the ball right onto the bat all the time and yet it's dead enough to kill all speed bowling. That swine Nicholls. I haven't scored runs at home *once* this season . . . all because he's been slipping work and sapping his vital juices with my Madeleine. No wonder he couldn't pull the roller. Too fagged!'

As a matter of honour, Spite said, he had been forced to resign the secretaryship of Netherpopham CC. I admired him. I said so.

Old Hacks had relaxed their 'old boys only' rule during my time at University, and I immediately suggested Spite made himself available for them.

He did.

Why are long-past summer days so hot, so rosy? Whenever I think of cricketing days of long ago I can only see blue skies — bluer than any I see now. My fellow players were comradely and jovial. The wickets were true. At some point in the day a Jack Russell would run on and yap at everyone in a friendly way. Runs flowed freely from the face of my bat. Evenings were hot and beery. I never dropped a catch . . . oh! I know the past all right — I've been there.

Spite played his match for OHCC on just such a day. We batted him number four. I opened with a swift twenty-two then dollied a ball to the covers. In those days I sometimes lost concentration between 20 and 30. Now I lapse between 5 and 10.

My fellow opener was out two balls later, Chinese cut onto his own wicket. He came back staring at his bat as if it had misled him somehow. Spite went in. He faced a teenage fast bowler, played and missed six times outside his off stump. His partner didn't score either. They stood in their respective creases for four overs, Spite playing and missing, his partner refusing to play at all. Finally the opposition brought on a slow bowler of pensionable age. Spite hoiked the first delivery down the throat of deep-mid-on. If the fieldsman hadn't caught the ball it would've put his teeth out. Even so he did some circus juggling before it stuck.

By the time deep-mid-on held the ball Spite was halfway to the clubhouse. Our visitors, GCHQ Minders 2nd XI, clapped politely. Spite threw his bat. Our captain of the day, George Jolly, went after him. He probably hoped to console Spite, who swore at the man. Spite threw his cap at us, his box at the scorers, his gloves at two small boys rehearsing football feints in the car park.

'Are you off?' asked George Jolly.

'Yes,' said Spite.

'Won't you have tea?'

'No.'

'Won't you field?'

'No.'

'*What* a disappointment,' said George, 'our batsmen normally stay on for tea and . . . er . . . *fielding*. You know?'

Spite didn't answer.

'Don't you want your bat back?' George asked.

'No. I don't need it.' Spite sat in his Ford Granada and revved the engine hard.

'Don't you want *any* of your things?'

'No.' Spite slammed the car into gear and drove off.

I had to get the pads back on Monday. Our wicketkeeper was upset, because the pads were his and he had to field in a sweaty old pair of batsman's ones from the club bag. He gave away twelve byes and blamed the pads. Our substitute fielder was George Jolly's twelve-year-old son who wore denims and a black teeshirt and held two catches. The boy, I remember, was not a success at school.

*

At lunchtime I went out, partly to avoid Coco, partly to see if I could get to the Patio Window Welko Wonderglass offices in my lunch hour. I had no car and it took twenty-nine minutes on foot. Should I have gone in I would have had two minutes in which to introduce myself before having to leave. I ate crisps as I half-walked, half-trotted back to college. I need hardly add that I didn't go into the Wonderglass office.

*

7.30 p.m. 'Have you done anything about your windows?' Elizabeth asked over supper (*supper* . . . a lot of haddock and potatoes with prawns sprinkled in it and cheese on top. Nursery food, bought in chain stores, cooked in the microwave. Disgusting). I've noticed over the years that as things wear and eventually break down they become 'yours' . . . i.e. 'mine'. We both decided on the double-glazing, but since it's no good Elizabeth calls it 'your windows'. I have to fight for an hour's use of the Ford Cortina, but should it refuse to start Elizabeth is as likely as not to phone and tell me 'your car's broken down. Won't you come and fix it?' I keep expecting her to point at some pair of sequined, high-heeled shoes with a hole in the sole and tell me 'your shoes need mending'.

'As a matter of fact I have, my dear. I went to their offices.'

That took her aback, I could see.

'What did they say?' Elizabeth asked.

'Nothing. I didn't go in. I didn't have time.'

34

Elizabeth gave me her ink-monitor frown and said, 'Why not?'

I left the table without another word and went into the conservatory, spying Elizabeth in the kitchen through the glass darkly, as it were. I was in a foul temper. I looked to where my seedlings should be. I have planted leek seeds and they should have taken easily in the relative warmth of the conservatory. Only one seed has proved fertile, though, and it lolls about the seed tray like a floppy, lonely, drunken sailor. Like a college lecturer outside a double-glazing shop window.

The reason I didn't go into the shop at lunch-time is as clear as the nose on my face. Elizabeth *knows* how far it is from Mugsborough College. She also knows that by its very nature a lunch hour contains only sixty minutes. She could have said something more tactful . . . like 'Didn't you have time to go in then, George?' but in her present mood Elizabeth would never think to be tactful. In her present mood she'd never stop to think that she was swanning around Bristol in the Ford Cortina while I was pounding the streets of Mugsborough.

I'll have to finish this tomorrow because I can hear her calling. In her present mood Elizabeth would cause trouble if she caught me writing this. She's probably put my fish pie in the microwave to re-heat as an act of conciliation. Lucky me!

Wednesday 16 February
Rain.

Yesterday's argument resumed. . . .

Elizabeth teaches art (or is it Art?) in a comprehensive school in Bristol. I do not begrudge her the daily use of the Ford Cortina. Though BR runs a perfectly good train service between Mugsborough and Bristol, I understand that Elizabeth, after her daily ministrations to the Beasts of Bristol, does not want to rub shoulders with the hoi polloi on her way home.

I understand all that.

I understand that anyone would need to re-establish their personal space after keeping control of thirty fourteen-year-olds doing remedial macramé, or after helping them find legal and non-violent uses for ex-washing-up-liquid-bottles and sticky-back plastic.

I understand *her* — but why doesn't E. understand *me*? She seems to think I've nothing better to do than hop around Mugsborough all day, picking up groceries and putting double-glazing salesmen in their place. Every morning as I leave home I find little messages by the door . . . '*1lb mince (beef), 1 tin Waitrose Consommé, 1 bottle Madeira (Jenny from the drama group's coming round and it's her tipple)* + *whatever white wine you'd like with supper*'. I'm a professional man! I feel such a fool slinking into the history room with my clinking plastic bags.

E. went to bed early this evening. The term is not yet six weeks old and she's suffering from the strain of caring for her charges — and what charges! Those who are not on probation are waiting to be tried, those not mentally deficient are morally corrupt, those who are physically present in class have been escorted there under duress by the Schools Attendance Officer. The police wait outside at chucking-out time to discourage the more blatant crimes of violence. Local buses won't stop within walking distance of the place, only slowing to disgorge pensioner-travellers at the jog-trot. If you can't run you have to stay on the bus till Kingswood. Oh no, I don't envy E. her workaday problems.

But why doesn't she understand mine?

Thursday 17 February
An early day for me, left college at 2.30 because my students had gone on a trip.

Success! When I arrived home there was a card on the doormat from P3W's service operative. He had called in response to my messages on the telephone answering machine. I'd missed him, but at least I now knew the answering machine system worked. I immediately rang P3W and asked for the service operative to call back in the morning. We'd leave the keys next door I said, after the beep.

Ten minutes later the phone rang. An almost incomprehensibly nasal-sounding girl with a London accent said that P3W operatives don't make appointments. He'll call when he's next in the area and hope to find someone in. Then she hung up. My only contribution to the conversation had been to give my phone number and agree that I was indeed George Lyall.

I sat and rehearsed all the arguments I could have had with her; that it's unreasonable to refuse to make appointments; that her salesman had made an appointment, the finance company rep. had made an appointment and the window fitters had made an appointment. I argued that P3W had a legal duty to fix my windows, that they had a moral duty to fix my windows. No matter how many times I rehearsed the arguments I always won. Every time I ran them through my mind I sounded smarter, cleverer. She was such a stupid girl. She could barely open her mouth (or nose, in her case) without I'd cap her comment with something clever. The debating skills one possesses within one's own mind are a wonder! Within the boundaries of my bony vault I'm witty, clever, sarcastic . . . always ready with the *mot juste*, the riposte, any French phrase you like.

I did not, though, ring Miss Nasal back and put all this skill into practice. I never do.

*

At 6.15 the Cortina drew up. E. leapt out, leaving the engine running, and staggered up the drive with one hand shielding her eyes from the porch light.

'Migraine,' she said and went straight upstairs. I rang her HOD at home and said things were looking bad for attendance tomorrow. E. never has one-day migraines. The HOD in question, a greasy little northerner called Jenkins, first complained about being brought to the phone in the evening, then spent half an hour whinging to me about some cookery technician being in hospital as a salmonella carrier; *what* a hard life it is being an HOD etc. etc. I don't know what his cookery technician has to do with Elizabeth being taken sick. About the only symptom people with salmonella poisoning *don't* have is a migraine. Jenkins spoke as if he thought I should personally do something . . . though I don't know what he expected. Should I make E. well? Incinerate his technician? Devise a short course (and offer it as an evening class) in epidemiology for his dead cookery students and their dying families? I recommended the man to read *Journal of the Plague Year* by Daniel Defoe, then rang off before he could ask me why.

Once the dread migraine has set in, Elizabeth is beyond doctors. I don't think she'd notice if Paul Newman, Trevor Brooking and the boys from Duran Duran were queueing to give her mouth-to-mouth resuscitation. We will be in for days and days of drawn curtains and weak beef tea. I will have to move into the study again (not necessarily a bad thing — I'll be able to keep the mono telly there tuned to highlights of the one-day games in New Zealand, as long as I only use the earplug for sound).

The slight cloud on the horizon is the fact that E. sometimes stages a recovery over the weekend, 'brightening' enough to be fit for work on Monday. It depends, but if she does 'brighten' the very process will involve refusing to let me watch cricket on the telly, instead dragging me up and down the Wansdyke for bracing walks. If E. only has migraine, she may well 'brighten'; if she has a syndrome she calls 'PMT', she probably won't 'brighten'; if she has PMT *and* migraine, she definitely won't (and I will have to lay on hundreds of hot-water bottles, dozens of paracetemols and as many women's magazines — hag's mags, as she calls them — as I can garner).

The omens do not look good. To be on the safe side (were the migraine and the PMT to be concurrent) I should spread straw on the streets, nab next-door's t.v. plug and gag all the children in the neighbourhood. I've never been very good at arithmetic, especially the female kind, and so have no idea which of the three possibilities outlined is actually the case.

I spent an hour in the conservatory, watering seedlings and encouraging leeks . . . more precisely I was watering seed-trays and encouraging the spaces where the leeks should be. If I fill the watering can very slowly even the tap doesn't make any noise. In the conservatory I practised my grip for a disguised leg-break I've been developing. These were the most silent things I could think to do.

Later I listened to Chopin waltzes with the headphones on while devising (with a silent fountain pen) part of a history course I've entitled, '*Cromwell to Castlereagh, conciliators*', and sub-titled, '*Could critical constitutional changes in earlier centuries have kept Catholic consciences centred on the survival of this country as a United Kingdom? Could we safely cede the Six Counties to a centralised Celtic State?*'

I've written a whole lecture in a similar, alliterative form — no one would notice, though, if I delivered it as-is. They'd just make notes, précis them and regurgitate an alliterative essay next week.

Sunday 20th February

Friday night, Saturday and today have been a continuing nightmare. Food has come either from the Freezer Centre or Penny's Pizza Place. I have had no time for myself, having to nurse E. in a darkened room all weekend. I haven't so much as glanced at the highlights of our tourists' Antipodean Antics (this time in Auckland). New Zealand won by six wickets without the help of the amazing R. J. Hadlee.

Elizabeth lies in bed all the time eating milk sops and reading *Harpers and Queen* by the light of a carefully shaded forty-watt lamp.

I spent quite a time perusing the magazine racks in the tobacconist's on Friday, carefully choosing her ladyship's 'hag's mags'. As a result of the time I spent there, an acne-d young male assistant (called 'Simon', he told me; though I know not why he told me) took me for a shy member of the dirty mackintosh brigade. I suppose he thought I needed help or encouragement. Anyway, he brought down a load of salacious rubbish from the top shelf . . . I never imagined such stuff might be legally sold over the counter in what I had heretofore imagined to be a perfectly respectable tobacconist's. Simon insisted on showing me the insides of the magazines, wherein young ladies, having quickly exhausted mere nakedness, seemed intent on showing me *their* insides too! If they'd spread their toes, turned their eyelids inside-out and stuck their tongues out, they would have been displaying every photographable part of their bodies (that is, photographable without resort to special film or trick cameras). As it was, 90% was revealed.

One girl was giving a man a come-hither grimace of exactly the type I've described above. The man wore black plastic clothes and a mask. He was carrying a rhino whip taller than himself in one hand and in his other hand a Black and Decker attachment the like of which is not stocked by my local hardware merchants. I should think it falls into their 'heavy duty' range and is only available to special order. The girl was tied to a lace-covered mattress and was surmounted by a Repin painting. I could imagine Elizabeth's response if I took her *that* to read! She hates Repin.

Ignoring my protest Simon showed me some more of these magazines. I nodded politely while his two teenage-girl fellow assistants made out not to look but giggled and blushed a lot. I felt sorry for them, having to work in such a place . . . but work is not easy to come by now for young people. I left the shop clasping a copy of *Waterways World*, two back numbers of *Wisden Monthly*, four ounces of wine gums and a sealed-for-life bag of Winter Warmers. But no hag's mags. I got those in W. H. Smiths, where you're never bothered by someone trying to serve you.

When I went back past the tobacconist's Simon waved at me, pointing to the small-ads bulletin board they keep. I made out not to see him. The shopgirls were clutching his arms and laughing, which I thought was very good-natured of them, given his insensitiveness towards their sex during my visit. I wonder if he treats all his male shoppers to such a sales pitch? If so, would he recognise the vicar in mufti? I don't know that the poor old thing could cope with the girl under the Repin painting.

Charlie Baker, in Business Studies, tells me that 'Simon' is an ex-student of ours, and that far from being employed in the shop he *owns* it.

'And he's only twenty-two,' Charlie said, with the air of a man imparting portentous news. With a mental age of seven, I thought. I believe that 'Simon' is not one of our more successful efforts, though I said nothing. It doesn't do to give too much of one's self away to colleagues, I have learned.

*

Yesterday (Saturday) I'd seen to my ailing wife (i.e. given her Ritz crackers and Ceylon tea with no milk — *her* menu — for breakfast); swept the house (hoovering was out of the question); shopped at Safeways; and was just about to slope off to the park for a jog as part of my pre-season fitness programme when Elizabeth's father, Eric, rang.

'I think I'm terminally ill, lad,' he said. He always calls me 'lad' or 'laddie', as if I were fifteen.

'Oh really, what's wrong?' I asked. I should have known better. Eric treated me to an hour-long lecture on his signs and symptoms. He has fainting spells, palpitations and sometimes sees double, he said.

'I feel the cold terribly, laddie, too.' All he'd need is consumption, an unrequited love and a quivering lip to turn him into one of Jane Austen's heroines . . . well, *nearly* all.

Elizabeth's father went through the rest of his symptoms, which appeared to range from bunching of the scalp to ingrown toenails, from chronic indigestion to shooting pains in his left bicep, from bulging eyes to (daily) alternating diarrhoea and constipation.

'I never know if I'm coming or going, lad, that's the truth. I'm having a terrible time.' He gave a little sob and was silent.

I have no sympathy for the man. I do not like him. Three years ago he gave me the worst Christmas of my life. He left Elizabeth's mother.

Now, I'm not a prude. I didn't care that he'd left her — heaven knows why he hadn't done *that* sooner. What I objected to was the timing of the leaving — Elizabeth and I were left holding the 'baby'.

We had gone to E.'s parental home for Christmas. In the end the holiday had more of the quality of a wake than anything else. At the time Elizabeth's father was a director and chief salesman of a light engineering firm in Corsham. He's since retired. His life had been one of wandering along the M4 (or earlier A4), flogging lightly engineered pieces. Methinks he wandered too much. Besides running along the English 'Silicon Valley', besides being a thoroughfare for floggers of high-tech, the M4 connects all the best spots for bad behaviour in the south-west. Elizabeth's father had taken full advantage of this fact for years. By judicious use of the

M4 a man can be rude in Reading and a naughty nag-backer in Newbury, he can sin in Swindon, booze in Bath, I-don't-know-nor-care-what in Bristol and still get home in time to change his shirt and eat supper in Corsham.

Elizabeth's father did the lot.

For *years*.

If there was a waitress to be seen home anywhere, Eric was your man. If there was a gin to be doubled, Eric was doubling. If a horse was running anywhere in the Home Counties, Eric would have an interest in the matter. Gilbey Vintners should have a medal struck in his honour. Bookmakers depended on him.

On the Christmas in question Eric excelled himself. We arrived at his and the Dragon's house on Christmas Eve. *He* came at 3 p.m. on the 28th.

'*Where* do you think you've been?' said the Dragon. Elizabeth was sitting on the stairs and crying quietly. I sipped a small sherry and avoided his eyes — he's *such* a scoundrel! I think if I'd even started to tell him how bad the last four days had been an ugly scene would have followed.

'Well?' said M-in-law, arms folded imperiously.

'Shut up,' Eric said.

'What do you mean?'

'I mean shut your face. I'm off.'

'Off?'

'Yes. Off. You're too ugly and you talk too much. I'm off. I'm leaving. Now shut up and get out of my way.'

She did it! The Dragon moved. Without another word Eric tugged his suitcase out to the Jag, threw it in the boot and snuggled down next to his floozie, a little peroxide and sequin number wearing hardly any clothes (despite the weather) and called — we learned later — Carol. She (Carol) is now twenty-two and was then *nineteen*! Ah, the vain fantasies of older men. Will I be spared them? I hope so.

The months that followed Eric's departure from Corsham were appalling. When E.'s mother wasn't staying with us, Elizabeth (who, like me, has no siblings) was staying with her. I don't know which was worse.

By summer and the start of the cricket season things appeared to have taken on some kind of equilibrium. The Dragon stayed in Corsham and appeared to be satisfied with small pleasures; waxing her furniture, yelling at little boys who cycled on the footpath near her lair, keeping the milkman waiting fifteen minutes while she scrutinised his bill and counted out her money in coins no larger than 5p. Once a week or so she'd get the bus to Bath and spend a hundred quid on clothes and sticky cakes.

Eric was busy rehabilitating himself with us. He'd shacked-up with an ever more seedy Carol in a flat in Swindon. Carol was, it seems, at one and the same time alcoholic and anorexic. When Eric brought her to lunch with us in late May of that same year she drank a whole bottle of my home-made carrot-and-orange wine, wouldn't touch her lunch and talked all afternoon about 'my career'.

'That's how us people in showbiz have to think, laddie, in terms of *careers.*' Eric had obviously convinced her 'laddie' was my name. Carol thinks of herself as a pop singer but says that because of her 'problems' she hasn't the chest for it any more. Eric, meanwhile, insisted on showing us pictures of Carol when he'd first met her. At that point in her 'career' she'd been a topless go-go-dancer wearing a rara-skirt in a large disco pub in Swindon. If the photos are anything to go by, she had enough chest then to be a disco singer, go-go-dancer, rara-skirt-wearer or anything else requiring a chest that she'd put her mind to. Looking at her across my lunch table, I couldn't help but wonder where the chest had gone-gone.

Later, Carol insisted on drinking vodka while the rest of us had tea and crumpets. Eric looked very shabby and we both felt sorry for him. Carol went to the loo and was so long Elizabeth went and caught her eating my deodorant soap.

As soon as they left E. was on the phone to her mother giving a blow-by-blow account which lasted nearly as long as the visit.

I didn't mind about the phone bill. I didn't mind about the soap. I didn't even mind that, after they'd gone, we discovered Carol had stolen (surely not eaten) two loo rolls. I didn't mind.

I *did* mind that she staged her subsequent suicide attempt in June. It was the day of our away game with Bellow's Merchant Bank. Bellow's is surely the poshest, most well-appointed wholly amateur cricket ground in the West of

43

England. It has a square like a billiard table, an outfield better than our own square, oak-panelled changing rooms and leather chairs in the bar. They supply everything free, do the best tea in England and there are so many lackeys around I wouldn't be surprised, *should* one drop a catch, to have the ball picked up by an obsequious little man in dark clothes who'd hand it back and call one 'sir'. He'd bow, too, of course.

Ah, the Bellow's match is a gem. It's organised by one of their directors, a Hackham's OB himself, who is very ancient and watches the match from a bath-chair on the clubhouse verandah and drinks gin. He always lays on supper too, with vintage wine and crusting port.

Such was the day on which the selfish and stupid Carol chose to attempt suicide. *Such* was the sunny blue day on which she chose to slash her wrists in Swindon. Frantic phone calls followed between a frantic Eric and my wife. Eric couldn't manage without Elizabeth. Elizabeth in her turn took up smoking again (immediately) and couldn't bring herself either to drive or to find a civil word for the man who had given up his plum cricket match to drive her — me. Eric merely had a nervous breadown in Swindon.

My troubles were not encompassed by Carol's suicide attempt, though. Oh no.

The very next week I twisted my knee while walking downstairs.

I had been waxing lyrical to Bertie 'Lend' Lease, our Senior Physics Lecturer, on the charms of the mature woman and why I deplored the use of young, insubstantial flibbertigibbets the shape of clothes horses as t.v. announcettes.

Bertie's lab is on the top floor of the old Grammar School building and I'd gone there after classes to make sure I'd got the technical side of carbon dating right (for a project one of my classes is doing on John Bright's speeches).

I *know* now that I'm never going to try to think about Mavis Nicholson *and* walk downstairs at one and the same time again. The floor loomed up, my knee twisted, I was stunned, and the next I knew I couldn't walk properly for a month. Imagine if I'd been thinking about Judith Chalmers!

My knee was so badly twisted I couldn't play cricket for a full month: *four weeks* during the very peak period of the season. I wasn't fit enough to umpire even. I couldn't walk very well and took nearly an hour to go up or down stairs. I drank very little, and all of it upstairs!

On the fifth week, when I could walk again and (I presume) Carol had more or less recovered, I was ready for cricket. We were due for the Hackham's OBCC's mid-season festival and double-wicket comp. It's comparable to some pagan rite . . . barbecue-ing, barrels of Somerset Cider, cricket, families, good-fellowship.

The day was hot (again). The sky was clear and blue (again). No cloud was in sight. My whites were freshly laundered and neatly pressed. I packed and unpacked my bag half a dozen times. I even remembered spare bootlaces. The season of the summer game is short and I had missed five full weekends. I was as keen as mustard. Elizabeth was even going to come.

This was the day on which Eric contrived to have his first heart attack.

I never played any cricket. I never tasted any cider. For the sixth consecutive playing weekend I was kept off the field. I was obliged instead to ferry E. and her mother to Swindon, where they sat around *his* hospital bed and cried with and at Carol. I've never been to Niagara Falls but I've a fair idea what it's like. Carol had her arms still in plaster (I remember the nicotine stains on the cast and the dew-drop on the end of her nose). Elizabeth had brought a box of man-sized tissues and, together with her mother, she went through them. Eric had obviously seen this cameo played on the silver screen many times before and acted his part to the full, lying there and looking grey-faced. I wonder if it was meant to be more literary — George Gissing, perhaps, expiring in some great dark French house, or Shelley's blue-lipped body washed up on a beach. Or pictorial — Marat bumped off in his bath, say. Eric knew. Eric had his scene foreseen.

I went downstairs and waited in the car park. Behind a big red-brick wall I could hear the click of wood and leather, polite applause, the sound of running feet, then '*Howzaaaaargh!*' The sun beat down on me. I sat in the car, wound the windows up tightly and, for the sixth Saturday afternoon running, listened to programmes for blind and crippled

45

people on Radio 4. Eventually I couldn't stand even that and read Neville Cardus's autobiography in an attempt to get away from cricket completely.

No wonder (and this is the point of these anecdotes) I gave the old buzzard short shrift when he phoned on Saturday and claimed to have been 'terminally ill'. I've had enough of him and his floozie and their 'terminal' illnesses. I told him so.

'I'm not interested,' I said. 'My wife, your daughter, is ill too.'

'Is it terminal?'

'No. PMT,' I said, with the air of a man who knew all about it. I knew that talking technically would fool him . . . though I do wonder sometimes what the initials stand for. I know what they *mean* — they mean that if I'm not very kind to Elizabeth all the time she'll sob and scream, that if I don't deliver hag's mags and belly warmers she'll snap at me. I know what the initials mean all right. I just wonder what they *stand for*. I remember feeling like that about l.b.w. when I was a little boy, or the new no-ball rule when I was older . . . or the inside of a vacuum cleaner for that matter. I know what they are and what they do, *ergo* I know what they *mean*. But *how* do they mean it?

'Wassat?' spat Eric, ever the diplomat.

'Women's problems,' I answered, 'not the sort of thing I'm about to discuss with you, especially over the public telephone system.'

'Is it terminal?' he asked.

'Of course not.'

'Well mine's terminal, laddie. Make sure she knows mine's terminal. Tell her.'

'Where's Carol?'

'Gone for my medicine.'

The off-licence, in other words.

'I'll tell her,' I said, 'when she's well. Call me tomorrow and give me a progress report on your terminality.'

'I'm terminal. I'll probably be dead by then,' he whinged. I didn't encourage him. I've had enough of his whinging.

Today Elizabeth stayed in bed. I read a history of the Vikings and made vegetable soup. In the evening she got up and watched Mastermind with me, during which I impressed by answering an obscure general knowledge question about Fulk the Black (or was it Eric the Red?).

One more leek has sprouted in the seed tray. Now there are two.

What an exciting life . . . especially if you're a leek.

Monday 21st February
The double-glazing repair man came!

Elizabeth was in and appears now to have overcome her physical condition enough to smile a little. She told me the repair operative had been 'hunky'. What a pity he hadn't been dextrous too, I thought, but said nothing. It seems double-glazing repairs are impossible on rainy days. I wondered if we must suffer leaky windows until July. The service operative (called Tom, E. tells me) applied half a roll of adhesive tape to the window, left the end of the tape hanging loose and then scoffed a lot of tea and biscuits.

'He can't come back for a week,' Elizabeth said, 'so I'm having next Monday off to let him in.'

It's a shame that E. should have to do this, but I suppose getting any sort of appointment from these people verges on the miraculous. If I'd been home when he called I'd have given 'Tom' a piece of my mind! I was pleased, anyway, to see Elizabeth returned so quickly to her normal self. It'll just serve Greasy Jenkins right if he has to do without the services of his ace CSE drawing teacher for a second Monday.

About 9 p.m. Patel came round with a complex cricket board game. He'd been to London, strayed into Hamleys and the board game was the result. *He'd* spent days studying the rules; I couldn't be expected to get the hang of it in the few minutes he'd allowed for me to mug up. The tourists won the rubber *in England* three-nil. That may well happen in a board game, I said, but not in life. As long as Mr R.D.(Z). Willis draws breath I can't see . . . well, perhaps I can. But not three-nil.

It was a good evening. Elizabeth, still jolly, flushed and recovered, brought us tea and biscuits at nine. I said, 'Just as if we were a couple of double glazing operatives.' And she went off in a huff and staged a relapse. No discernible sense of humour.

Patel won't get the business of camping on tour out of his mind. He showed me graphs which he says demonstrate the financial advantages a life under canvas offers the touring cricketer. He's even included the cost of hiring two butane stoves in his calculations. One stove is for an English breakfast, one for whatever East African Asians in general and Patel in particular consider a proper breakfast . . . lion haunch? scrambled ostrich egg?

I told Patel his idea would be a non-starter with Old Hacks unless his tent would have a bar and a bathroom. He insisted on leaving pamphlets from a tent hire firm in Bristol, though. Patel wants to make a firm booking soon. He says it'll give us full benefit of peace of mind (our eighteen-man ex-military job will be ours 'as much as if it were in my front room at this very moment') plus we will get a very decent discount plus George Jolly won't be letting his landlady friend down late in the season.

'We don't go there just so old Jolly can misbehave with the landlady while she fries our bacon,' I said.

Now Patel went off in a huff. I seem to be having that effect on people tonight.

Monday 28th February
Not so much rain today as of late.

Whoever would have thought the study of history dangerous? Leaving aside Hegel and neo-Marxian determinism, I would not. Nor, it seems, did Mr and Mrs Whortlebury when they sent their daughter Alison to Mugsborough College.

I'll never forget the face of the sister in the casualty ward when I explained that young Alison had sustained the contusions to her forearm while reading from Percy Bysshe Shelley's *Appeal to the Irish People*.

'Is it sharp?' asked the sister. 'Because only something sharp could've done this.'

Alison is a dumpy, action-packed virago who apparently spends all night dying her hair orange then gets up late and puts on odd socks (easily done . . . I've done it) and odd earrings too (I haven't done that and can't comment on how easily it's done). She's very good-natured, though, Alison, and I believe she fancies she's protecting me from the coarser elements in her/my class. I don't mind if it pleases Alison to believe that she's protecting me, but it's not true. I'm far too old a hand at this teaching game.

The group was doing Shelley as one small element in a theme I've picked out, 'The Development of the Romantic Revolutionary'. The theme runs right through the period we're covering — 1731 to 1927 — and I'm pleased to have come up with such a natty title. 'Themes' are all the rage in 'A'-level teaching at the moment and the possession of a good one is a feather in the cap of the teacher/lecturer . . . i.e. me.

I asked Alison to read at the front of the class. She did. She became excited as she read, striding up and down before the group and waving her arms . . . the romantic revolutionary holds a special attraction for Alison. An almost inevitable latecomer opened the door as Alison was in the midst of a particularily dramatic sweep. I believe she was exhorting the class to throw off the yoke of catholicism.

The rest is . . . history. Alison's arm went through the glass. Shelley ceased. The class screeched. The latecomer, I believe, will never come late again. A hammered glass door had exploded before his very eyes. I dismissed the group and arranged that young Carl Norton, a part-timer who only works mornings for us, should take my two afternoon classes — a YTS Catering Group Political Science Unit and dear old first-year Brit. Con.

There followed much waiting in the hospital, an acrimonious conversation with Alison's father ('Oh you mustn't blame poor George, Daddy, he's been abso-lute-ly *super* to me. Much more than a teacher ever has to be.' I could see that 'George' went down badly. Whortlebury Pater looked as if he might explode.) Back at Mugsborough College, I had an interview with Coco and spent an hour form-filling. I sincerely hope and pray no one ever dies in my class. I'd never surface from the paperwork.

I let myself off early. I stuffed my draft report on the injury to Alison Whortlebury into my briefcase, fobbed off my conscience with the knowledge that my classes were covered and with the idea that I was only going home to

49

work on my report in privacy and comfort, and plodded down to the bus stop.

For one hour this afternoon the sun shone. It seemed like it was the first time this year. The rays positively beat on me, on all of Mugsborough. The town seemed to steam. My feet swelled, my briefcase hung from my fingers as if it weighed 50lbs . . . 100lbs. A lot, anyway. My overcoat felt as if it would have done service on Red Square. February can be very hot. I sweltered. It all depends if there's any wind. Today there was no wind, not a whisper. As I plodded up The Glebe from the bus stop I noticed a P3W service van parked two hundred yards from my house. I felt like banging on the people's front door and calling, 'Don't do it, don't do it!' Unfortunately for the people in that house, I know the contract is signed, sealed and delivered by the time the service operative gets to your front door. You already have leaky windows.

I arrived home to find Elizabeth in her housecoat. She was looking much happier than this morning — she was positively radiant. I kissed her and remarked that the day had treated her well.

'Yes, *George*, it has!' she shouted. I *do* hope she's not been at the cooking sherry . . . it can't be genetically transmitted, my brain knows, but when I see my wife behave as erratically as her father I do wonder.

Elizabeth sat patiently on the sofa while I described the day's harrowing events: how the lifeblood gushed from poor Alison's young arm, her swooning classmates, my first-aid training, Spite's reaction ('*You'll* write the reports, Lyall'). I began to realise as I spoke in the safety of my home what a trauma the whole affair had been — then I felt selfish, self-obsessed.

'Oh Elizabeth, my darling,' I cried, 'and I've forgotten how dreadfully ill you've been. *What* a fool I am. You've been sick now for . . . how long? A week? Longer? Can you ever forgive me? I love you! I adore you! I want to *eat* you!'

These last words seemed almost to explode from me, rising from my breast like a great sob, tearing away from me, carrying my affection with them. I kissed her. Elizabeth sat back, smiling uncomfortably.

'Thank you George . . .' she coughed loudly.

I heard a distinct 'pingpingping' of hammer on metal.

50

Elizabeth put her finger to her lips. In her other hand I noticed she held a man's sock.

How surreal! that the presence of another person in my house should be indicated by a sock. I looked around the room. On one chair was my coat, on another, the jacket of a P3W Service Operative; on a third lay a shirt and one sock. The sock appeared to be a close relative of the one Elizabeth was holding.

'It's Tom,' she said, 'the double-glazing man. He was caught in a downpour coming here — very nearly a flash-flood, I should think. He's struggling on regardless and I've been drying his clothes out. They're nearly dry now.'

And they were. What a good woman my wife can be! Kind to a fault. I glanced in at the conservatory, saw the sweating red torso of Tom (he seemed as embarrassed as me) then went upstairs for a bath which I managed to drag out until I heard him leave.

There's something about earnest declarations of love that makes them best not overheard — even when passed between husband and wife. I found the fact that Tom must have heard me acutely embarrassing. I hardly even allowed the bathwater to splash until I heard the front door close.

*

7.30 p.m. Elizabeth's friend Christina came over. She only lives four doors away and is a large intense woman in her mid-forties married to a pale young insurance salesman called George. 'George II,' she calls him when she's with us. I don't know if the 'II' refers to the fact that I'm also a George or to the fact that her insurance salesman is her second husband. Whatever the truth of it, 'I've got a George II,' is a joke of which Christina appears never to tire.

Christina has never had a job. She has striven instead for a variety of 'causes'. During the time I've known her she's been a Samaritan, a CAB adviser, she's helped in a playgroup — the list just goes on. Christina gets 'into' things and drags Elizabeth (who goes more or less willingly) along.

Once Christina got 'into' exercise. For weeks she and E. virtually spat on the very idea of such a slovenly game as cricket. What they needed — and got — was the 'burn'.

Cricketers may swelter but they do not burn. Christina and Elizabeth burned by dressing suitably; oversized sweatsuits at £70 a go, spongy rubber shoes advertised as being suitable for running up side of the Grand Canyon but apparently not good enough in England to trot to the shops and back without the sole would part company with the upper. Once dressed, the ladies would present themselves in a converted mews in Bristol to be put through their paces by an underweight man-hater called Mandy. They burned to the very verge of incandescence. Mandy charged £5 for half an hour's over-exercise in front of a large glass mirror. Men, apart from obvious pansies, were banned from the groups — a fact for which I have often uttered sincere thanks. I think Mandy believed the sight of so many pounds slipping off would be more than men could bear. She was kidding herself, of course. I can manage without watching nearly naked bits of Christina flying one way only to be halted mid-flight and jellied back in the opposite direction. I have visual sensitivities.

The class folded completely when one of the 'obvious pansies' called Robert (*why* are they always called Robert?) was discovered to have been having concurrent affairs with half the class. The session at which this was revealed broke up amongst screaming, scratching, much wailing and anger and a stool thrown by Mandy at her large glass. In fact, it was an angry Mandy who was doing all the screaming, scratching and wailing . . . she was the only one of the single women there who *hadn't* been receiving Robert's attentions. It appears Mandy wasn't such a man-hater after all.

We now have the most expensive pink duster in the world . . . seventy quid's worth.

Next Christina got macrobiotics. Within a week so did we. I'm the sort of chap as can't stand brown rice — but brown rice wasn't the *half* of it! I wasn't allowed meat, was offered brown bread and sunflower marge instead. For breakfast I ate indescribable Swiss stuff which had been booby-trapped with little pieces of grit — my fillings have never been the same since.

One night Christina came round and explained the theory (she'd read a book on it). It seems you have to fill your face with as many indigestibles as possible, then run around a lot to work off surplus energy.

'What's the point,' I ventured, 'in eating indigestible food. . . .'

'*Fibre*,' she cut in, 'it's fibre.'

'Well, whatever it is, what's the point? Isn't it just a waste of energy to keep shoving in plateloads of stuff that don't do any good?'

'Wasting energy *is* the point,' Christina said. 'Getting fitter *is* the point. Getting a fitter, shinier, healthier phys-*eek*.'

Crufts came to mind. I don't want to look like an Afghan hound.

Christina's theory is wishful thinking. She has never in her adult life weighed less than fifteen stones. She obviously thought that if she could only stuff enough All Bran down her throat seven of these stones would get up and leave of their own accord. Who was I to disappoint her? I knew she'd move on to something else soon; nuclear disarmament, the Labour Party, Age Concern, the testing of cosmetics on animals, the Establishment of a Rest Home for Frail Ex-Insurance Salesmen called George. Christina is a true child of the nineteen sixties, right down to her Rolling Stones LPs and smocked dresses. Rather than seeking her métier, Christina has discovered her métier is seeking. I understand: I'm much more sympathetic than I have written here. Much may be learned by seeking. Except *why* does she have to drag Elizabeth round on her personal odyssey?

When Christina came round this evening I'd just finished 'Whortlebury, Alison, an accident report'. If I'd known I were so good at fiction I'd never have become a history teacher. For the benefit of the Education Authority I had to show the event which befell Alison as an act of God. God doesn't normally visit the history room during office hours and laying the blame at his door called for some strong creative writing. I was quite pleased with my effort in the end. God has yet to make his views known.

I went downstairs to find that Christina and Elizabeth had filled the kitchen with cigarette smoke — Elizabeth only smokes when she's with Christina and they know I *hate* it. They were about to start on their second bottle of wine. I've a nice bottle of Cape Red tucked away at the back of the garage, and one day I'll slip it to those two liberated ladies for their second bottle. It'll serve them right. I won't say till they've half-drunk it too . . . that'll set them gagging.

As I came downstairs E. and Christina were giggling. They positively burst out laughing when I came into the room.

'Hullo George,' said Christina.

'Good evening, Christina,' I said with excessive politeness. I am wary of her when she's in this mood. Suddenly she looked at the ceiling and said, 'Have you ever slept with a woman?'

They both roared. *What* a thing to say . . . in my own kitchen!

'What a silly question, Christina. Who are you sitting next to?'

Christina turned to me and smiled. I saw her face seemed blowzy and her eyes weren't focussed too well. I wondered if her greenhouse-raised hemp had been pressed into service again.

'Not you, George. Elizabeth, I was asking.'

I went away. I know when they're teasing. A long and detailed discussion of what went on in such circumstances would follow, with both women giggling a lot and looking at me from the sides of their eyes to see what effect it would have on me.

No thank you. I took my bat down to the garage, backed the car out and practised my forward defensive there, sheltered from the rain (which had begun again) and from prying eyes and laughing wives.

Not bad. Leg over quite nicely. I practised late cutting, too. *Very* nice. With no slips, no gulley, no bowler, no field, no boisterous colleagues standing on the boundary quaffing beer and cheering — with no *ball* it works a treat. I know, though, that come our practice match in April I'll try that late cut on the third ball because the ball's there to be hit. I know I'll feed the ball gently and harmlessly to a slip catcher. The only way he'll drop it is if it takes him by surprise.

Cackles of raucousness float from the kitchen. I grit my teeth and fondle my bottle of Cape Red. I will, I will.

54

March

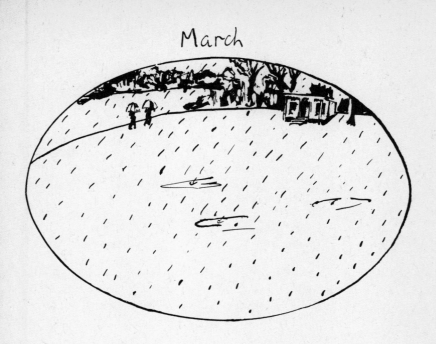

During March it rained.

April (showers)

Monday 11th April

The Easter hols are over. Those who have done nothing over the past fifteen days (leave alone the last eighteen months) will get their come-uppance in June. This is the term of the Exam Reaper.

It's also the term of the Summer Game. The Universities will start their fixtures on Tuesday week. Of course, they'll have to hope for a let-up in the monsoon we've had during March and over Easter . . . but the sun'll come out soon. I know. I feel it in my bones.

*

First thing this morning Spite bagged me in the staffroom.

'I want to talk to you.'

Then he disappeared without another word. I gave the room an open-handed gesture of exasperation. The room appeared more sensitive to my plight than fellow lecturers.

Not a word, not a movement . . . everyone buried his or her nose in a book.

At ten Spite came into the history room. That in itself was a rare event. What followed was *amazing*.

'Would you, er,' he said, 'would you, er . . . pop? . . . er . . .' His voice drifted off into the corner of the room, as if it were some ghost caught in the act of haunting and turned shy. I couldn't bear the suspense any longer.

'In to see you?' I offered.

Spite scratched his head and wiggled his tie-knot.

'Well, I think you could. I could spare a few minutes if *you* wanted to, Lyall. Yes, why not? If *you* feel you have to *you* can pop in to see me just about any time this morning.'

I went to Spite's office to see him. I followed him down the corridor. I thought it was a funny game he was playing but I was willing to go along for a while . . . he *is* HOD, after all is said and done. Who could fathom the enigmatic Spite? . . . not I. Perhaps it was a joke.

I trooped into Spite's stuffy, book-lined room and settled in the low-slung modern armchair he reserves for staff visitors. It squeaks as you sit, squeaks as you stand, appears to have been designed to cause underlings the maximum embarrassment. Once settled, your eyes are on a level with Spite's inkwell. Your status is demonstrated, your confidence undermined.

'Not there, George, old chap. Not there. Sit behind my desk.'

I squeaked out of my chair and sat in Spite's. At first I thought there was something wrong. I looked closely at him. His hands were trembling, he had egg on his tie and his eyes had a vacant, slightly doolally look. He pulled his right ear whenever he spoke and his brain rushed from subject to subject like a headless chicken.

Spite was completely normal.

I allowed his voice to drone over me like some lost Spitfire. Since boyhood I'd been forced to stand on the far side of the desk. Now I had the occupant's view. My thoughts were of boy's newspapers, war-mags, the Bodyline Series, D-day, Elgar and the Pleistocene period . . . a culture perceived but not grasped. When I was a boy I thought the occupant of that chair must know *everything*. I looked up at him. The papers on his desk were a disordered mess and so was he. Dishevelled, uncombed, babbling.

'I wanted to talk to you about Dexter, George. That's why I've asked you to sit in my chair. My chair is now your chair. You're in charge. I am a mere caret, you that which is carried. I am scoria, you lava. Am I clear?'

'We're flotsam and jetsam?' I ventured. He shook his head. I didn't understand. He wants me to take responsibility for a boy called 'Dexter'. I don't know of him. Is Dexter a christian or surname? Is Dexter in fact a boy at all? I waved my hands to indicate nothing could be clearer. Clear? I should cocoa . . . I had no idea.

I noticed from the papers on Spite's desk that he appeared to be reworking reports on students written in the grammar school days of the early sixties. Both the papers and his hands were covered in red ink splashes. The guilty red pen (an old fashioned 'dipper') lay on the desk.

'Who's Dexter?' I asked. Spite lowered himself into the staff chair and rubbed his face with his hands. He mumbled to himself.

I turned over some of the papers. I recognised names, classmates. He may even have been re-writing mine. Maybe the past has been a mistake! Maybe that's what Spite's rambling was about. . . . 'There's been a terrible error and the school has let you down, George.' I could picture it . . . I went to Oxford, got a First, married a beautiful banking heiress whose family thought I was the best thing since sliced bread and therefore showered me with money . . . *jam*-ed me. When I wasn't making millions in the City I was playing soccer as an amateur for a first-division club, when I wasn't being adored by my family I was off scoring 100 and taking five wickets in Karachi . . . no! *MCG*! I wrote brilliant history textbooks during my plane journeys. The BBC would ask me to make programmes on the ancient world. I'd be like Michael Wood, only with looser trousers (my sense of propriety, don't you know). John Timpson would be phoning me at home for live comments on world events for the Today programme. . . .

All this could have happened. It all depended on Spite having written different words in nineteen-sixty-five. '*Lyall is a brilliant boy. His wit is coruscating. He turns in twice as much*

59

work as he's asked for and it's all of the very highest quality. He speaks five languages fluently, has done original work on spoken Ancient Assyrian and has all the makings of a top-drawer research historian. A pleasure to work with. Warmly recommended.'

I turned over the papers on the desk, looking for a 'Lyall'.

No 'Lyall'.

No heiress, no MCG, no Today programme. I don't like John Timpson's jokes anyway.

Spite spoke. 'I believe your mind has been on higher things, George.'

'What, Spaight?'

'Call me Edmund.' He waved his hand expansively. Until that moment I'd never even guessed at what the 'E.E.V.' part of E.E.V. Spaight, BSc, MA, stood for. I'd never dared.

'I'm wondering how that desk fits you, George,' he went on.

'Not badly,' I said. Could this be a hint?

'There are, of course, channels of communication between this desk and the history room. History's remorseless progression must not be allowed to go unobserved by those of us charged with the responsibility of overseeing it.'

Is Spite a Russian? I thought. Is he telling me he's about to defect? I couldn't imagine what his drift was.

'Mm,' I said.

'It's all to do with communication. Dexter knows all about communication. That's how he had that wonderful double-act going with Parfitt.'

'Parfitt?'

'In *Karachi*, George. You know about Karachi.'

I nearly passed out. I'd *thought* about Karachi, but never mentioned it. Perhaps Spite had some gift. Perhaps there was something in all this 'communication' business. MCG would be next. Could Spite fix it? What about the heiress?

Spite picked his nose, then stared at me for a long time.

'You know all about that, Georgy boy, don't you?' he said. 'You're in the know. You've been initiated. There are direct lines between the history room and Coco's office. The lines of communication have already been set up. You've been initiated.' Spite's eyes glazed over again and he went to the window. Below his office is what was known in my day as the 'quad'. Nowadays it's called the 'square' . . . an achievement of the comprehensive system. I wondered what was passing through Spite's mind. He'd seen it all change . . . he's watched it happen. Where once pimple-capped boys walked respectfully and learned Tennyson off by heart, teenage couples now saunter. Sometimes the teenagers go into clinches so intense it seems only a couple of tyre levers and a bucket of cold water would separate them. I'm sure Spite thinks of me and my generation as having brought all this about.

He turned quickly from the window, dragged a hundred or so files from his cabinet, dumped them on the desk and asked, 'Which amongst these should we initiate, George? You're my friend . . . you tell me. Who should we allow onto our level?'

None of the files belonged to a student who'd left our care more recently than 1973. I said I had a class to prepare, I'd give the matter some thought and let him know later.

I never got a chance. Two large men came for him . . . they didn't wear white coats but they drove a blue Mercedes converted into an ambulance and they were accompanied by the former Mrs Spaight. Spite went with them with the look of a man walking out to mount a tumbril. Miss Trimble should have been laid on to knit by his side. I could have played the *sans culotte*.

I mentioned this to Coco when he called me in.

'I think Miss Trimble has enough on her plate with the Home Management course, George, without entertaining poor old Spaight.' He paused for a moment, furrowing his brow. 'You never said you were musical before. We could have used you in the orchestra.'

Both by training and inclination Channel is a scientist. He also hates cricket. I wouldn't have much time for the man, except that he's College Principal.

He said, 'Spaight won't be back for quite a while, you know. Very sad business.'

I nodded sagely. Why has everyone started calling me 'George'? They made-do for years with plain old 'Lyall'.

'How d'you feel about being HOD, *pro tem* . . . till all this business has cleared itself up. I thought if you would I'd ask our part-timer, young Carl Norton, to fill in for you on the same basis in the history room. Much better than getting some "supply" in.'

The rest of the interview passed in a haze. I only know I agreed. Ten minutes later I was settling in behind *that desk*. Half an hour later I'd cleared the files away and was dictating my first letter to ~~Spite's~~ *my* secretary, Jane Trump. (I'd always known she was a . . . well, a big girl, but stuck in this tiny room with her it's hard to know where to look for the best. If I stare at the desk I seem furtive, at the ceiling seems dreamy, out of the window pre-occupied. For now I've settled for staring straight into her face . . . but I think that will eventually seem flirtatious. The main thing is not to stare at her . . . bosom. But that's easier said than done in such a small room.)

*

I rushed home at 5 p.m. My news caused no ripple of excitement. Elizabeth said I'm too career-minded and that's always (crude word)ed me up. I'm not career-minded. What of the servant who hid his talent? I wouldn't like to be in his boots when his Master tallies up. You don't get on first-name terms with the Principal and promoted to HOD (Temp) by revealing your genius only in the home. You need to shine in the workplace. A lot of people could do worse than follow my example.

I told Elizabeth all this and she shouted 'Fascist!' and stormed off to her confidante, Christina. I settled to do some work on the club accounts which Biggs had dropped by for me to have a look at; it seems Coggins (our former Hon. Club Treasurer, now serving time in Pentonville for . . . well, just *for*) has left the books in the most awful mess. Biggs thinks Coggins may have filched some of the club's lolly. I can't tell. I can't concentrate; ten minutes later E. was back yelling that if I was so jolly clever I could get jolly P3W to jolly come round and fix our new jolly windows and not send that lazy useless jolly lump called Tom to do it. Then Elizabeth went back to Christina's.

The word she used wasn't jolly.

I don't think Christina and her home-grown hemp have a

very positive influence on my wife. They bring out the worst in her.

*

For fun I looked up E.R. Dexter in *Wisden*. After some detective work I established he holds the record for a 4th wicket stand for England versus Pakistan. 188 runs at Karachi. His partner was P. H. Parfitt and the year was 1962. Was Spite's poor tortured brain trying to tell me something?

*

I must do two things tomorrow. 1) I must make time to go to the Citizen's Advice Bureau with a view to small-claiming P3W. 2) I must remember the sub-committee on Hack's finances meets tomorrow night at Biggs' house. I must not forget either of these . . . no fail.

As soon as I sat down to look over Biggs'/Coggins' accounts the phone rang. It was Eric, intimating mortality for all of us and for himself in particular. I gave him Christina's number and told him to watch his lip because she's a BOSS agent. 'She knew all about you and that black belly-dancer.' That shut him up.

Early to bed, early to rise; all that. I have a number of responsibilities now.

E. came in at 2 a.m. and was somewhat the worse for wear. I feigned sleep, fearing she might want to continue our 'discussion'. I don't want to listen.

Tuesday 12th April
A heavy day for me. First job was to install Carl Norton as my sub. First-year Brit. Con. put on a show of being deeply disappointed, which was kind of them. I couldn't help but think, though, that it was unfortunate for Norton to be faced with such an argumentative first class . . . 1st-year Brit. Con. are a veritable group of Stoics. I have every confidence he'll cope. But what a test! At least he already knows them slightly.

Second job was to go through Spite's 'pending' tray (the tray does not in fact exist, only the concept; Spite's 'ins' and 'outs' are looked after by Jane Trump). This meant being locked in Spite's little room with Ms Trump and her bosom and my unsteady gaze for some time. The thought had crossed my mind the previous evening, so, displaying the sort of foresight a potential manager of my abilities should display, I stepped off the bus a stop early on the way to work, went in to a garage and equipped myself. I've bought a pair of mirror-lens sunglasses, the sort Lee McQueen or Steve Marvin might wear as he mounts his Harley Davidson . . . oh yes, I know all the technical details. No one can see where you're looking from behind those.

The sunglasses were an instant success.

'Very fetching,' Jane Trump said, 'I know these neon lights can be very trying for sensitive eyes.'

Exactly. Ms Trump's only mistake was to believe that the sensitivity was in the eyes and not the brain that lay behind them. The trouble was, having worn the sunglasses for Ms Trump, I felt it would look out of place if I took them off for the rest of the day. This meant interviewing two departmental members about timetables in dark glasses, telling off a truant (irregular or non-attender, we call them now) in dark glasses, feeling my way to the lavatory because of the dark glasses and keeping my office lights on all day because of the dark glasses. Charlie Baker of Business Studies called in to borrow our BBC Micro — theirs has gone on the blink — and asked if I'd been in a fight. Alison Whortlebury found some pretext to come in ('It's about these forms, George.' 'I'm afraid it'll have to be Mr Lyall while I'm HOD(Temp), Alison') and told me the specs made me look moody, mean and domineering . . . I took them off at once and told Alison she'd be late for her dance class. Green leotards don't leave much to the imagination.

I gave myself an extra half-hour for lunch, made a leisurely phone call on my private line to Elizabeth (who'd gone sick from work — over-exhaustion, she calls it), then pottered down to the Citizen's Advice Bureau. A young woman in a heavy woollen dress gave me a class history of Britain and suggested it was my fault somehow, that I was oppressing the builder (the poor dear) and, anyway, didn't I even admit that the windows leaked just a *little* bit and they'd sent an operative to fix them four times. . . . Wasn't that reasonable? What more could I want?

'I want my windows fixed,' I said. 'We're in the fourth month of the year and I've had nothing but the run-around about them.'

'Keep your shirt on, dearie.' The young woman in the woollen dress lit a cheroot and thumbed through some papers. I noticed she had a very short haircut and badly bitten fingernails.

'The man who owns the double-glazing company drives an Audi Quattro,' I said, 'I've seen it outside his office. I have to make do with a Ford Cortina 1600L while he's got five hundred quid of my money.'

'I hardly think an extra five hundred pounds will get you from a Ford Cortina to an Audi Quattro, Mr Lyall. I don't see how this interferes with your relationship, anyway.'

I pointed out I had no *relationship* with the builder. She asked was I or was I not claiming he owed me money. I said he did owe me money and what's more he was a wretched artisan fit only for employment in a nationalised industry.

'Like teaching?' said the CAB woman, drawing deeply on her cheroot and blowing smoke as if she were an excursion steamer on the GWR. She was right of course . . . howzat? Dead plumb. L.b.w. . . . h.w. would be more accurate. The CAB woman suggested I talked to a solicitor under l.a.

'Los Angeles?' I asked.

'Legal Aid.' She sneered and stuffed some pamphlets in my hand.

'How can I get l.a.?' I cried. 'I'm a HOD(Temp).'

'Tough luck.' She shut the door in my face and put up a 'closed' sign.

Later I saw her going into Safeway's arm-in-arm with a very pretty girl. I always have a bad effect on that type . . . I don't know why.

When I returned to College I swore I never wanted to see another acronym. Outside my office door was a deputation from the YTS lecturers wanting to know how secure CG funding was for next year. Also there was Mrs Spaight, wife of my barmy HOD. I fobbed off the YTS people and chose to see her.

There is nothing cryptic, mnemonic, acronymic or otherwise obtuse about the ex-Mrs Spaight. She's approaching fifty, much younger than Spite, very beautiful in a mature sort of way, dresses expensively, has a throaty voice and a manner which would give one to understand she owns the world. I let her sit in the staff chair (I'm surprised it didn't catch fire); so doing being my only chance of not being hopelessly outclassed. Ex-Mrs Spaight — 'call me Madeleine' — let her body ease back in the staff chair. She looked totally relaxed. It was *I* who was forced to lean over the top of my desk to look into her face as we spoke. Madeleine positively simmered. No wonder the gardener turned into a Mellors . . . all that digging around in the soil and feeling your roots on a sunny day in Netherpopham, then out slips Madeleine carrying a pot of tea and wearing only a white cotton dress and a sultry look. She was a good many years younger then, too. No wonder the track at Netherpopham CC went to pot. Mellors must have thought he was in heaven.

'Dashed hot, isn't it, Mellors? I thought we might pop down to the Rhododendron Dell and put some hormone powder on our root division propagators.'

'Ooh ar, milady. Oi'll just loosen off me braces.'

I can just see it.

Madeleine Spaight said to me, 'I'm *so* sorry old Eddie's gawn and took Tom-and-Dick.' She slurred her words like the Prince of Wales. I had no idea what she was talking about.

'Eddy?'

''im indoors. He's gawn and fell orf the beam again, hasn't he George, my old china? It must be a real pain in the aris for you.'

'Who's Tom?' I asked.

'Don't know any Tom.' She frowned and brushed her skirt.

I put on my sunglasses and said, 'It's not your horticultural friend, is it?'

'Horticultural . . . oh *him*. No George, that was *years* ago. Nicholls. He was a right boring old lump of Tom Tit. My present escort flogs jam jars down the Goldhawk Road.'

'I wonder if we could go back to the beginning, Mrs Spaight.'

We did. It seems she falls out with her escorts from time to time and, therefore, a fair number had interposed themselves between Mellors/Nicholls and her cockney friend in the Goldhawk Road. Mrs Spaight is a sentimental type, though, and hasn't allowed Spite to drop completely off her horizon. When she discovered last summer he was in the public ward of Mugsborough Infirmary talking gibberish (he'd kept *that* one under his hat . . . no mean feat in a small town) she'd immediately put him in a private nursing home until the start of term. Now she was doing the same again, she'd come for some of his books and papers, and — I guessed — a little inside information on this institution's attitude to the stricken Spite.

I was able to put her mind at rest. I took her hotel phone number, assured her that I, on behalf of the department, would keep in touch, all that.

*

Straight home at five. I felt like a damp rag. By five-thirty I was wearing my plush red carpet slippers and sipping a large scotch. So this is what it's like at the top. Pressure, harassment, all-day decision-making. Other people's lives in your hands . . . *that's* responsibility.

My lifemate didn't want to know. I brought my own slippers, poured my own scotch, fetched my own newspaper. Elizabeth's only comment was, 'I hope no one we know saw you in those stupid sun-specs.' (I'd forgotten to take them off.)

I told her about the day anyway. I often find the best policy with Elizabeth is to carry on regardless at whatever you want to do or talk about . . . she usually comes round in the end. Tonight she didn't get a chance. I drank my whisky, told my day's story to her ladyship, cast a quick eye over the *Mugsborough Evening Chron.* (Ring Road Rumpus. Vile Vicar Vilified. How Sexy Sabrina, The *Chronicle's* Own Easter Bunny, was 'Initiated' by Mugsborough Tory Party Chairman) and then I was off, dashing down the drive to catch a bus into town again.

'Don't "bump into" Madeleine Speight. Cricket meeting and straight home,' Elizabeth called after me.

Sometimes she *does* listen, even when she appears not to.

*

Hack's Finance Sub-committee was originally set up as a diplomatic method of stopping Albert, our Honorary Mr President, buying any more Indian quarter balls or pairs of left pads. By and large it's worked well, though an unscrupulous score-book sales rep. managed to get him to buy a gross of all-season club score-books by promising Albert a 50p per book discount and insisting the deal was closed by 4.30 the same day. Albert used his initiative and, knowing there wasn't enough time to convene the OHCC Finance Sub-committee, wrote a cheque there and then. Including the two spare books the club already possessed, we now own enough all-season score books to last until 2129 AD (or we could give one per season to each club officer . . . in which case we'd all go down with writer's cramp but the books would run out in a mere twenty-five years or so). Every now and then Patel gets angry enough to say, 'But I don't know *why* you did it, Albert.'

And Albert smiles serenely and says, 'We secured a very respectable discount by buying at the right time, that's why.'

There's no point in arguing further, and it's only Patel's peculiarly insistent brain that wants the matter raised at all.

We have nowadays, though, a serious problem in the club . . . and good fortune has meant that Old Hack's has a purpose-built committee, i.e. us, good old Finance Sub-committee. Coggins — I'd rather hoped not to have to soil my diary with that name again — *has* left the club books in the most awful mess. Poor Biggs, with his bank-teller mentality, is afraid that he will be held responsible for the club funds. He sees the Finance Sub-Committee as the body that should have responsibility for the mess and, I have to say, I think he's right. The problem is that Biggs is the sort of chap who isn't often right, and therefore makes the most of it when he is. He's sent each of us, Patel, Albert, Brian Cook in Tenerife (or wherever), George Jolly and me, a long, complex document which runs to fifteen or so pages and is for the most part covered in numbers.

I'm not much of a man for arithmetic . . . double-entry

ledgers fox me completely, and I've a feeling that only Patel will have any idea what it all means in the final analysis. After all, computers are closer to book-keeping than history is.

I arrived at Biggs' terraced house at 7.30 sharp. Only Albert was there, and he'd come to offer his apologies . . . it appears we'd clashed with his darts league management committee annual meeting, and he felt they couldn't manage without him (more likely he's spent five hundred of their smackeroos on dartboards with only nineteen segments — at a very respectable discount — and needs to break the news to them).

Off went Albert. I was stuck for an awkward half-hour with Biggs in his parlour. Mrs Biggs — a small mousey woman wearing the only paisley pattern pinafore dress I'd seen since my grandmother passed on to the great scullery in the sky — offered tea, then digestive biscuits, then more tea . . . I half-expected to be offered bread and butter dredged with sugar. Mrs Biggs — who surely wasn't over thirty — was straight out of a Hovis advert. The sixties and seventies had never happened to her.

Biggs himself wore a pair of grey, coarse woollen trousers, a faded blue cotton shirt and the heaviest pair of button-on braces I've seen in years. One would have thought he'd only ten minutes since he'd left his steaming loco at Mugsborough Rail Depot (Goods) instead of spending all day closeted in a bank two hundred yards from his home, counting filthy lucre.

'Would you like to see my den?' he asked. 'Perhaps we could hold our confab there.'

The 'den' was a box-room at the rear of the house. It had a small desk and chair, a minute sofa and a bottle of scotch. I cleared a lot of letters beginning 'My Dear Comrade Biggs' off the sofa and sat. I wondered would I be offered any scotch.

'We won't start on the books matter till the others come. I don't want to go through it twice,' he said.

Neither did I.

'I'll fetch some glasses.' He stood with the scotch bottle in his hand, then pointed at a red banner which covered one wall of the little room. 'I see you've noticed that.'

'Noticed it' was an understatement. It was a battle flag, inscribed with the name of the regiment (National Union of Bank Clerks, Tellers and Comptometer Operatives, Local 315 (Mugsborough)) and a series of dates calculated to give the impression that Tolpuddle, Peterloo, Taff Vale Railway, even the ousting of the Heath Government would be as nothing were it not for the intercession of the union under whose name they appeared.

'Our branch banner,' he said, and disappeared out the door. 'I'm officially responsible for it.'

I think he's gone a bit dotty, to tell the truth. Every time I see Biggs he inveighs against capitalism in general and usury in particular without ever stopping to think who provides the cash for the terraced roof over his and Mrs Biggs' heads. It's *so* unselfconscious; the kind of behaviour I find it very difficult not to despise. Biggs owns his house, wears a suit to work, is called 'Mr Biggs' by his supervisor . . . in these circumstances it's pretty dotty to force copies of *The Ragged Trousered Philanthropists* and *The Condition of the Working Classes in England* on your visitors. He once tried to get George Jolly and myself to go to a four-day Eisenstein festival in Crewe . . . heaven knows why he thought *we* were the most suitable recruits.

But what makes Biggs *really* dotty is that he keeps pursuing a claim to be Hack's regular wicketkeeper.

Has anyone ever met a sane wicketkeeper? I haven't.

It all started for Biggs when young Tommy Butcher, our wicketkeeper, fell sick with mumps last season. Biggs stepped in at the last minute for one match and did a creditable job. I think he only let go four byes and fumbled one possible snick (but that was travelling). We must have been too fulsome in our praise. Butcher was obviously out for the rest of the season, a quick decision was needed about who should take over, eventually Chas Smith — one of our irregulars — agreed to make himself available for the rest of the season. He's a decent keeper and we all thought we'd found a good arrangement.

Biggs was furious. He wandered around invoking gods and demons both ancient and new . . . has anyone ever heard Roger Tolchard's name used as a curse before? It's not a pretty sight.

'Do you know who T.G. Evans was, Lyall?' he asked me after our next match.

'Of course,' I replied.

'Well how many wickets did he take in all?' he said in a most aggressive manner.

'I've no idea,' I said. 'What a wacky question to ask a chap out of the blue!'

'That's what I mean about the people in this club, Lyall. They know nothing about wicketkeeping. I've made quite a study of it over the years. How many did Parks catch in all?'

Paul Peterson, our vice-captain, had joined us and answered the question for me. 'Parks caught a thousand and eighty-nine and totalled one-one-eight-two. He wasn't much of a stumper. Evans caught eight hundred and eleven and totalled one-oh-six-oh, which makes him a bit sharper close to the stumps. Chas Smith played in a league side last season. He's quick and I'd have thought a man who turns the ball as sharply as you would have been dying to have him "standing up" for you, Biggs.'

I was astonished. It was quite a performance even from a clever dick like Peterson. Was there no end to the man's talent? Biggs was quite bowled over, and could only manage a rather nasty, 'Sold many doorstep policies lately?' — a reference to Peterson's involvement in his father's insurance brokerage. Biggs was certainly having none of the 'man who turns the ball as sharply as you' flattery and I don't blame him. No one bowls plumber than him — it's the slowness of his delivery and the impatience of the batsmen which gets him all his wickets.

Anyone who takes fifty wickets a year off such indifferent bowling should think himself a lucky man and plod on with the indifferent bowling. I think his mere four byes as a keeper was a fluke.

Biggs came back — interrupting my thoughts — with no glasses but with Patel.

'Good God!' said my little Indian friend when he saw the banner.

'Smart, eh?' said Biggs.

Patel brought apologies from George Jolly. No one expected Cooky to fly in from his Spanish resort, so that left us three as the Finance Sub-Committee. I thought we'd have a brief discussion, then we could hop off to The George and Dragon for a swift half.

How wrong I was.

'Order, order,' Biggs called to us, 'I call this meeting of Old Hackhamians' Cricket Club Finance Sub-Committee to order. Apologies for absences first, gentlemen.'

'Don't you think we can dispense with the formalities, Biggs?' asked Patel. 'Let's just run through the figures, see if we agree and write a note to the club committee to the effect that this committee has sorted the matter out.'

'You're out of order there, Mr Patel.'

Patel bit his knuckle and we both listened to apologies for absence. Then we listened to notes of the last meeting and passed them on the nod. Then we went through the fifteen pages of numbers. Patel and Biggs seemed to understand them well enough. I agreed when asked to, disagreed when asked to, that sort of thing. Most of the time I studied the battle banner. . . . Why the enigmatic word 'Brighton' woven in one corner? What *is* a comptometer?

'And so I think we're able to put the motion to this meeting in the form that "This committee recommends the club committee and its officers accept the report of this committee and its officers in the form it is presented in by this committee and the said officers. Should any further investigation be thought necessary then this committee recommends that the club committee and its officers charge this committee and its officers with responsibility for the investigation, bearing in mind that this committee and its officers have the necessary expertise and has already been able to produce a report which is in the negative with regard to the questions posed by the club committee and its officers about the matter in hand" . . . well?'

'Yes,' said Patel.

I said yes too, but it wasn't the answer Biggs wanted.

'*You* have to put it,' he said, '*I* can't. I'm chair. You put it, George.'

'Put it?'

'The motion. Then Patel can second and we can have a vote.'

I tried.

'This committee recommends that that committee accepts

what this committee recommends with regard to what that committee asked us to do, and that. . . .'

'Are you serious?' Biggs broke in. 'It has to be put officially, not full of gobbledegook like that. Let Patel have a go.'

Patel fared no better. After extensive but unsuccessful coaching we solved the matter by voting me in as temporary chair, letting Biggs put the motion and Patel second, then quickly swapping Biggs to the chair so that he could repeat the motion in the form voted-in in just the manner a 'chair' ought to use. Patel glared at me when Biggs raised the matter of any-other-business. He didn't need to. My brain was spinning and I still hadn't had any of the scotch Biggs kept waving in front of us.

We headed for the front door, pausing only to refuse free copies of *Militant* and allow the much downtrodden Mrs Biggs to lick everyone's boots in her shy little way.

'I *do* hope you've brought an umber-ella, Mr Lyall. I wouldn't laike you to get wet, Mr Lyall. Have you had any supper yet?'

'No, I haven't,' I said.

'Well, Mr Biggs and I can give you some if you would prefer . . . though I s'pose Mrs Lyall will have something cold on the table for you when you return to your own home.'

'Something like that.' I smiled at her. I thought she'd appreciate a smile more than most.

Patel laughed so much I felt like booting him down the road. I only relaxed when we'd installed ourselves in the King Charles Bar (as in 'hid here' . . . what a furtive life that man must have led) of the Royal Hotel and equipped ourselves with a half of bitter each.

One matter puzzled me still.

'Patel,' I asked, 'did you understand all that back there?'

'You mean did I understand what was going on?'

'Yes.'

He smiled and sipped his beer before saying, 'Yes, George, I did understand it. A very simple matter really. Anyone could have understood it, I thought. Why do you ask?'

'I just wondered . . . did we decide that Coggins had or hadn't made off with the club's loot?'

He laughed and at first wouldn't tell, but Patel's a good-natured soul at heart, and eventually — after a good deal of teasing me — told me I'd put my name to a document which said that Coggins had not made off with Hack's money but had left the accounts a right shambles. I was relieved. I'll be even more relieved if Coggins doesn't pass this way again . . . as I'm sure will the Mugsborough Screw and Die Works, his erstwhile employers.

One strange event *did* take place in the Royal Hotel. At about twenty past ten, when Patel and I were just finishing our fourth half, Madeleine Spaight came in. She was obviously somewhat the worse for wear and she plonked herself right between the two of us and asked, 'What'll you have, boys?'

I introduced her — I was forced to — and pointed out that closing time was fast approaching.

'Not for residents, it's not,' she said. Her speech was definitely slurred.

'Well, I'll have to be going,' said Patel.

'*We* will,' I corrected him. We supped up and stood. Mrs Spaight stood too, only this time she hauled herself up with the greatest difficulty. It appeared she'd sprained her ankle when she sat.

'Could you help me upstairs, George?' she said.

'I'll get someone from the hotel to.'

'Oh no no! I don't trust them. *You* help me.'

I shrugged my shoulders at Patel (who was beaming behind her back) and took her arm. Mrs Spaight swayed a little and smelled like a crate of empty whisky bottles. When we got to her room she draped herself round me, said the ankle was most painful and would I open the door for her?

I did.

Once I'd got the door open she said would I help her over to her dresser?

I did.

Then she said she had to stand to get her dress off and couldn't do the zip as she would be using her hands to support herself. Would I be a dear and unzip the zip?

I was and I did.

The dress fell to the floor, Mrs Spaight stepped out of it and walked over to her bed (with her magically cured ankle).

She shivered, held out her arms and said in her dark, throaty voice, 'And now, George dear, will you come here to me?'

I did not. People can become temporarily deranged by grief, and I thought her (albeit ex-) husband's condition may have had this effect on her. Whatever her game was, I didn't want to play. It would be immoral and uncharitable to take advantage of a middle-aged lady who had been stricken by alcohol and grief. I did not intend to.

I went downstairs. Patel was nowhere to be found. He'd grown impatient at his two-minute wait and driven off. I had to wait on the taxi rank with a lot of drunks — among which there were four of my students, in pairs and hugging each other like limpets, plus half a dozen squaddies of the 'red beret' variety who acted out the storming of Port Stanley for the benefit of us poor weak-willed namby-pambys who'd never served in the army and therefore had no idea what 'life is all about' (as one put it).

I didn't get home till 11.30. I was *exhausted*. And starving . . . though of course Elizabeth hadn't left something, cold or otherwise, on the table for me. Predictable, but I have to admit I prefer Elizabeth's predictability to Mrs Biggs'. The latter would be like drowning in syrup. Or tea.

On the telephone table was a note. *'Biggs rang and said he'd enjoyed tonight and has decided to tour this year and camp out with you and Patel. Does this message make any sense to you? E.'*

If I were to be given the choice I'd say that I didn't understand and didn't want to. I had no choice though, and I have to say the message is ominous.

Wednesday 13th April
7.00 a.m. Breakfast.

E. is particularly jolly.

'Good time last night?' she asked.

'If you can call a visit to the Mugsborough branch of the Worker's Revolutionary Party a good time, yes.'

'But you went to the pub with Patel after?'

'Yes. Yes . . . that was all right. Just Patel and me,' I lied.

She gave a little trill of a laugh and said, 'Didn't bump into Madeleine Spaight after all then?'

'Her? Ha. ha. No. Just a quiet drink with Patel and straight home.' *Two* lies!

I munched my Weetabix like a man waiting the return of the Mission to Delos. Perhaps if I munch very slowly and quietly no one'll notice I exist. Perhaps the boat will never come in.

'What time did you get here, then?'

'Oh . . . eleven, I suppose.'

A great lump of Weetabix had turned to concrete in my throat.

'Funny,' she said, 'I thought it was later than that.'

'Oh.' Munch munch. 'Why do you ask about her, Elizabeth?'

'Who?'

'Madeleine Spaight.'

'I'm only teasing, George. Charlie Baker called with a fantastic piece of gossip. He said he'd heard a rumour that she was thinking of moving back into the area and that she'd been at your office at college asking advice. I think he just wanted to try the gossip out on you, get you to confirm or deny. You know.'

'Yes.'

'Well?' She scraped furiously at a piece of burnt toast. I'm sure Elizabeth burns more slices of bread than she eats.

'No. She didn't ask my advice about moving to Mugsborough,' I said, thankful to get back on to the truth again. I so hate lying to my wife, whatever the cause. 'Have you made any hemlock?'

'What?'

'*Coffee*, sorry. Coffee.'

I buried my head in a week-old copy of the *Times Ed. Supp.* and drank my hemlock quietly.

Wednesday 27th April

I have not had as much time as I would have liked in which to write my diary. You can always find an excuse *not* to do something.

The business of being HOD(Temp) has palled somewhat. I think you've got to be something of an education *apparatchik* to enjoy it. I'm obviously not . . . I sometimes even catch myself yearning for good old 1st-year Brit. Con. The job appears to consist mainly of reading incomprehensible notes of incomprehensible meetings on obscure subjects, then formulating a policy based on these documents and delivering it a) in condensed form, verbally to staff, and b) in extremely long-winded form, both verbally and on paper, to meetings. As I read out my thoughts at these meetings I see the other members' (town councillors/principal/governors/other HODs) eyes glaze over and their brains switch off. I'm not allowed to shut up and sit down though. Oh no. I have to burble on for the right amount of time. To do less would be rude. Then someone gets up and reads his or her thoughts out, and my eyes in their turn glaze over with all the others. You could slip fantastic policies and ideas through at these meetings — should you be so inclined. Perhaps one day I will.

'. . . drone drone drone drone and as well as new tiles for the college shower room I thought we could put in a dental surgery where any little blighter caught cheeking could have his teeth removed and his face sewn up drone drone drone drone drone and instead of a telling-off for anyone who doesn't do his homework we could tie them up and shoot them drone drone drone drone and the County Architect's estimate for the shower room tiles is on the enclosed sheet, page four, section b, drone drone drone. . . .'

Perhaps this is how the Machiavellian Coco managed to get his amazing exam policy *in situ*. Rather than having a load of chumps failing their 'O' and 'A'-levels and getting us a bad name, Coco has managed to arrange things so that we only 'sponsor' those who have a good chance of passing. Whether anyone else takes the exam or not is, of course, up to them. Then, when the results come out, we only publish the ones we've sponsored and everyone says, '90% pass rate; *what* a good college Mugsborough is, and *what* a perceptive Principal Mr Channel is'. Just exclude the thickos . . . the simplicity of it makes it beautiful. A brilliant example of lateral thinking.

And dishonesty.

I think it's the dishonesty I dislike most about being HOD. Until recently I had no idea how much was involved. You have to sit in your office while one staff-member after another breezes in and breaks down before your very eyes.

'I *really* need to know now, George, what *are* my chances of promotion?' And this from someone who came into the profession on five 'O'-levels and a Cert. Ed. when we were desperate in the sixties. What can I say?

I say, 'Well, keep applying . . . just look, you've got *loads* of experience.'

It's revolting. I can hardly wait till Spite sorts his marbles out and comes back, though Coco tells me that's not going to be until the autumn.

I can hardly wait for the cricket season to start. Last week the good men and true of Cambridge dashed out from under their brollies to have a quick thrash with Glamorgan. It was inevitably drawn. Oxford did the same with Lancashire at the beginning of this week with the same equally inevitable result.

It's very depressing.

*

5 p.m. This evening should have heralded the start of a new season for OH's. I had booked a practice pitch with Mugsborough College's head caretaker, the surly Bert. Our own pitch is shared with Old Hackhamians' Rugby Football Club and has yet to recover from the ravages of scrumming. If reckless promises made before the Easter hols were to be believed, we were to be seventeen — an ample number for a pre-season double-wicket warm-up. Instead I found myself faced with the prospect of spending the evening in the conservatory, tending to my tomato seedlings and listening to Radio Three. A quick shufti at the newspaper showed it would have to be a Stockhausen song-cycle. Does *anyone* like Stockhausen? And they keep putting the licence fee up.

Carl Norton, my junior full-time (Temp) colleague of two weeks' standing, had noticed how morose I had been in the afternoon. We were sitting in the staff coffee lounge during afternoon break. Rainwater beat against the windows.

'Something wrong, George?' he said.

I tried to make out it was nothing, offered him a rock cake, put a good face on things.

'Cricket, isn't it George? Leather-on-willow, all that sort of thing.'

Am I so transparent? Perhaps not. Carl has a keen mind. He was at Oxford (Pembroke), was awarded an upper second. He shows remarkable perspicacity for a man of twenty-two. Ah, the value of a good education. Of course I too could have been an Oxford man, but I lacked parental encouragement. My parents said I would have been desperately unhappy so far from home and instead bade me study at the local polytechnic where I met people who talked about 'imperatives' and 'historical perspective'. After following their bidding in good filial fashion for years, my parents died on me and now I'll never be a Pembroke man because I'm too old and stuck in Mugsborough. Also I didn't get the 'A'-level grades . . . but I might have with the right encouragement.

Being HOD(Temp) isn't much consolation.

'Yes, Carl, you're right,' I said, 'today was to have been our pre-season warm-up practice match. Saturday should be the Hollwellians OBA match . . . fat chance! And it seems only days since we were listening to reports of the tour on the World Service.'

'I can't get the World Service,' he said.

'Nor can I . . . that's not the point.'

A clap of thunder shook the room. The sky looked blacker than ever.

'Let me buy you a pint after work, George, cheer you up,' Carl said.

What a nice man! I don't usually go to pubs during the week unless it's connected to some special event but I agreed to go with him. Rules are made to be broken. I wouldn't like to slight a young man with a refusal, anyway. He is new to this profession and unaware, perhaps, that such offers usually come from the top down. He'll learn.

*

I wish I *had* refused. After working on till five-oh-five we departed the college in perfectly filthy weather and waited a further fifteen minutes for the bus. When it finally came we were shoved unceremoniously upstairs by the conductor, who seemed unimpressed by my arguments against passive smoking. The bus company have a bare-faced cheek to charge full fare in such circumstances.

When the conductor finally chose to stroll upstairs I discovered that he's the father of a boy I had occasion to discipline some years ago and seems (the father, that is) to have taken to an almost pathological hatred of me, snatching my five-pound note and asking sarcastically through twisted lips if I didn't have anything smaller. I don't know why the father responds so . . . his son has a good job as an apprentice lavatory cleaner in an engineering works — and this at a time when jobs are hard to come by for unskilled young people. The boy has, by his appearance when we meet in the street, forgotten me and the disciplining completely.

Carl and I arrived at the Station Hotel like orphans from the storm; soaked, bedraggled and fully eighty pence per man poorer from our contact with the bus.

I might have guessed that Jenkins would be there. He was leaning against a corner of the bar with some of his building-site cronies. When he saw me he slammed his foaming pint onto the counter so hard I thought the glass would break, then charged across the room like a rhinoceros.

'**** me, it's Georgy. George, you old ******, how are you doing?' He always addresses me so, though I've told him heaven knows how many times that I hate it.

I introduced Carl, though I could see that he too was struggling to keep a look of disdain from his face. Carl confided in me once that his family make him a small allowance . . . such a man is hardly likely to have met the likes of Jenkins before!

'Phillip Jenkins, Old Hack's cricketer and admirer of your companion, the incomparable Lyall,' said Jenkins, cutting an exaggerated bow and displaying a head of thick brown hair clotted with emulsion paint.

'You didn't make the AGM Jenkins. Strange for one so keen on the game.'

'Prior commitments, Georgy, you old wooden spoon.' He held out his hand and Carl took it and said, 'How d'ye do.'

Very Pembroke, I thought. Of course it was wasted on Jenkins.

'Jenkins is a builder,' I said.

'Labourer,' Jenkins corrected, 'and I can't labour in the

rain. We can't play cricket in the rain, either, can we George? Course not. What will you have to drink?'

Jenkins was drunk. I don't know (and don't wish to know) how the landlord of the Station Hotel stays to rights with his conscience — let alone the law — but he keeps a notorious 'afternoon' pub. Phillip Jenkins had been 'afternooning'.

Carl and I had two small bitters from him, the cost of which to us being that we were forced to listen to Jenkins' hoary old jokes. I need hardly add that these were expressed in the most foul language. In a short time Jenkins moved on to some of his cricketing anecdotes — with himself, as might be imagined, in the starring role. When Jenkins has had a few bevvies his tales get taller and taller . . . he ends up hitting the ball harder than Trott, bowling faster than Trueman and fielding more nimbly than Constantine.

I must say I was not a little surprised when young Carl offered to buy Jenkins another drink. He was taking politeness to a fault.

The conversation turned, as I had guessed it might, to my batting.

'I remember a time,' said Jenkins, 'when old Georgy here could be trusted to carry his bat through an entire innings.'

Which was simply *untrue*. He does *not* remember such a time. Jenkins is not a proper Old Hack and hasn't been with us long. Harold Simpson, our former Club Honorary President, allowed his son to introduce Jenkins some four seasons ago. We all quickly lived to rue the day — except Harold who went into surgery for his prostate problem soon after and died under the knife (we now play on windy days with the Harold Simpson Memorial Lignum Vitae Bails). Jenkins has never seen me 'carry my bat', but like everyone else I'd been forced to watch him 'open his mouth'. It's forced on us because Jenkins is the most prolific wicket-taker the club's ever had, and so — against the better judgment of some of us — Brian Cook and Paul Peterson have insisted we play Jenkins when he's available. *I* wouldn't play him ever. I'd like to shoot him.

Truth is of no concern to Jenkins, and in his inebriated state his imagination appeared to run riot.

'Used to open, George did. *I've* seen him open. Don' s'pose we could let you open now, Georgy my old china . . . *oh* no!

George only ever *closes* now, doncha, George? Ha ha ha ha ha. Averaged a bit less than some of us for the last few years, 'aven't you? Still, s'pose you'll do better this year, eh?'

Jenkins clasped his hands together and waved them, windmill fashion, about his head. He nearly dislodged a dozen whisky glasses hung above the bar. Jenkins reeled over till his face was close to mine, then shouted, 'Someone shut that door!'

'This year in particular?' Carl asked. Sometimes the boy's very innocence can be exasperating.

'The new Gunn and Moore he's gone and bought. You've bought a new bat, haven't you George? Big as Ian Botham's. If that don't get George back into double figures, nuffink will.'

'Botham, as any television screen will witness, Jenkins, uses a Duncan Fearnley,' I said.

'Who was talking about his bat?' Jenkins retorted.

Carl drew deeply on his beer and said, '*Double figures?*'

Oh dear. If I had been a newspaper reporter, say for the *Sunday People*, I could have made an excuse and left. Instead I had to suffer the indignity of having my 1982/3 batting average discussed in the public bar of the Station Hotel, Mugsborough. Batting averages can only be fully understood in a sober forum where the attendant circumstances can be considered and weighed. The Station Hotel, Mugsborough, on a rainy April night, being full of sozzled builders, could hardly be proposed as such a forum.

I feel I have brought this on my own head. I had let Carl know of my passion for cricket during informal moments in the staffroom and had failed — rather foolishly — to correct the impression he had somehow gained that I was 'quite something with the bat'.

Mea culpa. 7.56 is not 'quite something with the bat', and I am sure I have fallen in my young colleague's estimation.

*

7.30 p.m. Arrived home to find a note from Elizabeth. 'Gone to Drama Workshop'. I didn't know Mugsborough had a drama workshop.

I put a one-portion pizza in the microwave and went into

the conservatory. I have planted out my leeks, though they're so small they should properly be called 'drips'. Now I'm on to tomato seedlings . . . and they're not doing very well. I have kept the little darlings warm and watered, given them plenty of light . . . still no joy. When I prick them out they wither. Perhaps 'Marmande' simply isn't suitable in this latitude. I've bought specially patented trussing clips too. I can't think what else I'd use the clips for . . . starting a clematis farm?

I can't believe Jenkins could have been so rude to me. He can be foul. There are depths to which he will sink which are as yet unplumbed by the rest of mankind. When I think of all the rotten things I could say about him! But I won't.

*

Last season Jenkins deliberately bowled at the head of Ponchester III's number four bat no less than *three times*. When the unfortunate man was caught behind fending off the third of these deliveries Jenkins' reaction was merely to stuff the ball into his pocket, stalk to third man (ready for my next over) and glower. The number four bat walked to the pavilion in silence. Number seven, Ponchester III's next man in, walked to the wicket in silence. None of us OHs had the nerve to clap. When the 'man in' reached the bowler's end Jenkins pulled the ball from his pocket, roared like a wild beast and threw it so that umpire, new batsman and Patel (who'd come over to offer me some friendly advice) had to dive for their lives. I stung all my fingers catching it . . . though if I'd let it bounce and then caught it I'd never have heard the end of the matter from the Beast in the Deep.

He's a brute, and his rudeness to me in front of young Carl emphasises it. I don't think he's the type of man who should drink.

Now that I recall, it was only after his fourth pint on the night of the Ponchester game that Jenkins' twisted logic revealed itself. It seems he's overheard the opposition at tea ribbing their number four bat, 'would today take him to 1000 runs for the season?' I remember Jenkins strutting round the bar-room as he related the story, poking his finger aggressively into his own hairy chest.

'Not off my ****** bowling it wouldn't.'

He'd started bowling beamers when he reckoned the Ponchester man would have been on 996.

'Tosser!' he'd called the batsman to us . . . an unfortunate soubriquet, given the circumstances.

*

9.30 p.m. Patel telephoned just as I was going to bed.

'There will be no selection committee meeting tomorrow, Mr Secretary.'

I knew that. One look at my waterlogged lawn was enough to demonstrate it.

Patel is, like many of his countrymen, an absolute stickler for correctness. He would, I knew, be conscientiously working his way round the selection committee, telephoning and telling each man the obvious. Such is Patel's attachment to the 'correct form'.

'Thank you, Patel,' I said, 'how kind of you to call.'

I was yawning.

'That's okay, George. Since you're Hon. Sec. I take it I can leave it to you, eh?'

Then he put the phone down. Since I was still mid-yawn, I didn't get out even the smallest peep of protest. It was clear my early night was not to be. It took twenty minutes to track down the other three members of the selection committee and they took my message to convey the obvious.

Thoroughly awake again, I began to plough through some essays on the Civil War.

When I first took on the business of being HOD(Temp) I made an absolute rule that I'd keep teaching a few classes a week. I'm beginning to wish I hadn't. Most of the essays were under a page in length, but one boy has written what I can only describe as a novella about the *American* civil war. I'll have to see him. On checking the register I can't find any 'S. Crane' in that class. Perhaps someone's mixed the essays up.

*

11.30 p.m. The telephone rang again, waking me. It was
Jenkins.

'Hullo, George. Dunnerserlecshun yet?'

'What?'

'On'y, I fought we could include your pal, Carl.'

There was a lot of yelling in the background.

'Are you drunk, Jenkins? Do you know what the time is?' I
said.

'On'y, your pal Carl, 'e says 'e bowls slow lef' armers an'
can turn a few.' There was much laughter behind Jenkins.
One of his friends, I presumed, telling a dirty story. Just
about their level.

'On'y,' he went on, ''e reckons 'e can bat a bit, an' all. An' I
says to 'im, we ain't got oner them. Well we ain't, 'ave we
George?'

I could hear the laughter behind him again. I said, 'Is Carl
there?'

Jenkins put his hand over the mouthpiece and said quite
distinctly, 'He wants to know if you're here.'

I put the phone down. Sometimes it's more a question of
drying out the players than the pitch before the start of play.

*

12.45 a.m. Elizabeth returned, showered and then sat on the
edge of the bed, dripping in a towel. When I asked why she
was late she said, 'Painting stage flats.'

She lit a cigarette (which she knows I hate in the bedroom)
and claimed she needed all the lights on to be able to read
Cosmopolitan. When I remonstrated with her, she said we
ought to have separate rooms. I came into the study to write
this diary.

When I went back, she'd lit *another cigarette*.

'That'll kill you,' I said.

'Something will, George, I'm sure,' she snapped.

'I didn't know there was a drama group,' I said. 'Not
anywhere local.'

'Methodist Hall.' She stubbed her cigarette out and was at
once asleep. I had to get up and turn off the lights. I lay
awake till 3 a.m. staring at the ceiling. So much for early
nights.

Thursday 28th April
I'm so tired.

Rain again. When I asked the surly Bert could I book a practice pitch for next Wednesday he laughed and walked away. When I approached his assistant, Charlie, he said, 'I've known you here since you were a little boy, George Lyall.' And he laughed and walked away too! What is it about groundsmen and caretakers that turns them into such superior creatures?

Saw Norton. Have decided to re-introduce some element of formality into our relationship, therefore 'Carl' has become 'Norton'. I think this is only right and proper. It was remiss of me to be so informal so early in our professional relationship. I had thought I was doing the boy a kindness.

'Hallo, Norton,' I said.

'Who makes your rock-cakes?' he said. I think the alcohol must have turned his mind. He looked pretty rough, but I said nothing more.

Saturday 30th April
9 a.m. Patel and I went to the sports centre, where we had booked what is known as the 'missile area'.

'We've come for our "cruise",' I said with a smile to the girl on the cash desk. She was a sour-faced type with little sense of humour.

'Two seventy-five, then.'

Not a titter, just slapped my change on the counter without even a common 'thank you'.

The missile area is a space twenty-five yards long and two wide. It was occupied by archers when we arrived. Heavy curtains prevented them from sticking a flight into a volley-ball player. The archers packed their stuff when we showed up, but since we had booked the 'missile area' from nine till ten at £2.75 per hour I do think they should have cleared off before we came. Their clearing-up took five minutes of our time and when I pointed out to the archer-in-chief (or whatever they're called) that they'd occupied 22.9 pence worth of our time he sneered at me and walked away.

What sort of man plays bows and arrows into adult life?

Someone verging on the mentally retarded, it seems.

My new Gunn and Moore is a very nice bat. Patel has bought a polyplastic, saying it does away with knocking-in, oiling, all the tedious parts of cricket bat ownership.

'How many nights did you spend knocking that in, George, when you could have been doing something more useful?'

I tried Patel's bat and I'm convinced the ball has a tendency to slide off the surface of it. Patel tried mine to feel the difference, though he's a man of such slight stature he couldn't get a proper backlift and so had no real way of telling. He would really do better with a colt or size 6 bat . . . though he won't be told.

Before we'd had time to do much more than discuss the relative merits of our bats Robin-of-Sherwood was back . . . this time accompanied by a tracksuited council official.

'Not in them, sport,' said the official. Was it a code?

'What do you mean?' I asked. The archer was looking very smug.

'Not in them there shoes, not in here.'

I own a rather smart pair of grey canvas bumpers or, as they are now known, 'trainers'. They have a sort of stickle-back sole to stop one falling over.

'Why not?'

'They've got black soles. We don't not have no black soles in here.'

'They've got grey soles,' I said.

'Don' matter. No street shoes, no black soles, no coloured soles allowed in here.'

'But these *aren't* street shoes,' I reasoned. 'They're pukka trainers, built and purchased for the job in hand.'

'No mate. Strict instructions. No black soles on the "sportolux" surface. More than my job's worth, that's the truth mate.'

'How should I play then?'

'White soles or bare feet. That's all.'

I thought of offering him fifty pence to turn a blind eye, but he didn't seem the sort.

*

9.45 a.m. Patel drove me home. I have learned the lessons of cricket too well. Getting my foot across to the line of the ball is second nature, and of course, given the fact that I was using my new bat, it was only a question of time before I was hit by a ball. My little toe is swollen to twice its normal size.

Elizabeth was furious.

'Where's the car?'

'Outside the sports centre,' I said, 'I couldn't drive. Patel ran me back.'

'Well I need the car. I have to go to a casting meeting.'

Meetings are the bane of a professional person's life, of course. Patel drove her back to fetch our car. I listened to a tape-recording of this morning's 'Sport on Four'. I don't know why someone should be so proud of having played cricket for Glamorgan. It's like playing rugby for Holland. And what qualified him to lead England? How should our friends in the valleys respond if I turned up at Cardiff Arms Park with my boots and a request to play rugby for Wales? It's the thin end of the wedge. After Welsh and Scotsmen came South Africans. No doubt one day we'll field a Chinaman in an England cap, all because his father was once a short-order cook in Blackpool.

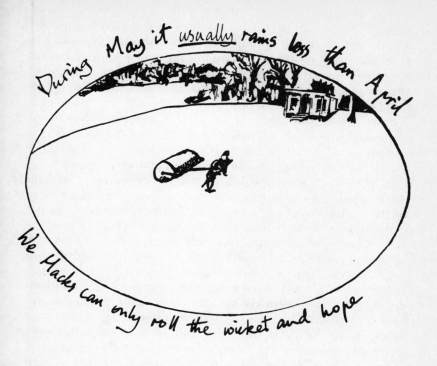

During May it usually rains less than April

We Hacks can only roll the wicket and hope

Thursday 19th May

During May it has rained too. I'm surprised, in fact, that I haven't developed webbed feet. If I could find eleven men with oily coats, impervious parts and safe hands they'd do a treat right now. I could get a game of cricket up with the penguins in Bristol Zoo. Gloucestershire, who've yet to finish a home match, would probably want my eleven oily-coated cricketers to sign professional papers. Or the penguins.

I've written little because I wanted to write about the summer game: how can you play cricket when the summer refuses to arrive? It's very frustrating. We've done everything except *play*. Every Thursday we hold a team selection meeting, usually consisting of a permutation from Paul Peterson (vice-Cap), Patel (Other Member), Biggs (Treasurer), George Jolly (stand-in Captain), and myself. We solemnly pick a team, inform the players that night, prepare transport — lifts, all that sort of thing — work out whose turn it is to lug the club bag there. Then we sit back and watch the rain.

Usually by five-thirty on Friday night we're phoning round and telling every one the game's off . . . though once we did it on Saturday morning and on another occasion Patel and I stationed ourselves at the club gates for Saturday lunchtime, thereby missing the soccer round-up on t.v. We stood like two old ladies waiting for a bus, clasped under one umbrella. No one was stupid enough to turn up in such a downpour anyway. We wasted our time.

We've had some nice little trips out. We've been to three or four of the villages round here, got changed and then sat on the pavilion steps waiting for the downpour to ease. You get a lot of time to talk on these occasions. People discover splits in the seams of their boots, hairline fractures in the wood of their prized bats; they dig up the seams of practice balls with their thumbnails, fumble about in the club bag for 'that pink plastic box I lost during the away game at Merryton last season . . . or was it the season before?' The last from Biggs — what has he been using since he lost it? I've noticed the conversations quickly turn sour, sarcastic comments fly back and forth, nasty little cracks about 'that catch you dropped in Netherpopham in nineteen-seventy-one'. We never play any cricket, though. Once we even went as far as to toss up, inspect the track and then throw the ball to each other on the boundary while the other team's openers padded-up. Then the rain came down. Afterwards we all felt obliged to say to each other that we always knew it would rain.

We don't have to select a team for this Saturday, anyway. It's Cup Final day — *FA* Cup Final, that is — and there are no fixtures. We did have a fixture for some years with a nonconformist Jewish team which just couldn't pass up the opportunity for a Saturday game — *any* Saturday game — but they folded eventually after they were set upon by the rabbinical equivalent of Jesuits in the course of a needle match with Yeovil Tax Collectors Charity XI. It must have been a rare and disconcerting spectacle: a pitch invasion by thirty elderly men in big hats and shawls singing psalms and heaping blessings on the Tax Collectors' wicketkeeper (who'd held two difficult catches and precipitated a collapse in the nonconformist Jewish team's batting). The Tax Collectors grabbed their stumps and ran, the David Ben Gurion

Memorial XI (Secular Wing) simply ceased to exist and our FA Cup Final day fixture vanished with them.

No. This Saturday, like everyone else, I'll buy a few tins of lager, park myself in front of the t.v., choke when they sing 'Abide with me' and try to get enthusiastic for one or other of the sides, Brighton or Manchester United. Patel will phone just as they're about to kick-off and not stop chatting till halfway through the first half. He hates soccer. Elizabeth will hide the infra-red thing for the t.v. about her person and keep channel-hopping just to annoy me. I will curse the thirty old men in big hats and shawls and regret the passing of a good day's cricket.

Does Steve Foster of Brighton and Hove Albion wear a bandage round his head in an effort to elicit sympathy? 'Oh look, that poor thing's hurt himself already.' Perhaps he keeps it there as a kind of first-aid box; certainly one or two of Brighton's opponents must have wondered as to its purpose when they suffered Foster's robust style of play. I mentioned this to Charlie Baker at lunchtime and he said Foster's not allowed to play in the Final on account of his rough play in the past. I sometimes wonder if soccer is such a man's sport after all. I wonder what would happen if Malcolm Marshall were excluded from a cricket cup final on account of he's bowled a lot of beamers in the past?

I'm not much of a soccer man myself; FA Cup Final, European Cup Final, England games on the t.v. and that's about covered my interest. I wouldn't miss a game of cricket for it. Madness overtakes the entire nation on Cup Final day, and I'll have to sit and watch soccer with everyone else. It's pretty galling, I must say, to sit in one's own front room watching soccer while the sun is shining and cricket might be played; my new batting gloves are still in their wrapper, my new bat is yet to be unsheathed and my balls grow daily more dusty even enclosed as they are in a little bag of their own.

We will pick a team for Sunday, of course, but I don't hold out much hope of play. The outfield is waterlogged and doesn't drain quickly.

Monday 23rd May

Manchester United and Brighton drew, we didn't play at all. It's how everything seems to be going lately. Saturday afternoon was frankly boring, no matter how excited Jimmy Hill became and tried to dress it up as 'the big match'.

I spent Sunday listening to Elizabeth 'doing' her lines for the play she's in. It's a translation from the original Afrikaans and is all about 'angst and weltschmerz' brought on by the 'situation there'.

'I thought "angst" and "weltschmerz" were German words.' I said.

'Well?'

'But I thought this play was Dutch.'

'Afrikaans . . . well?'

'Well?'

'Well?'

I gave up. It worried me though, this business of South African depression.

'Who translated it?' I said later when I went into the study to give her a cup of tea. E. had recorded her fellow players' lines onto a cassette, and she now wore a Sony Walkman which was playing the cassette.

'Tek your hends owf me, yew stinking cop!' she yelled. I almost dropped the cup . . . then recovered. E. has belonged to several Drama Groups — each of which has closed, though I intimate no fault of my wife's here — and always learns her lines this way. It sounds like you've got a ghost locked in an upper room. Once she sung a great chunk of *HMS Pinafore* like this, all chorus stuff and therefore missing the lead parts. She was in the study and I was paying the milkman at the front door . . . it says a lot for the professional code of milkmen that he didn't bat an eyelid. They (milkmen) must see some strange sights in the course of a week's work. He did give me too much change, though, which I think is as close to a nervous breakdown as a milkman will ever get. His bottles rattled as he walked back to his float. He should have heard Christina rehearsing a badly out-of-tune *Valkyrie* when she belonged to the opera society; the bottles would have jumped out of their crate and his yoghurts turned sour.

*

12.45. Coco took me to lunch . . . an unexpected privilege. We have a training restaurant in the college, put there specifically so our catering groups get full work experience. The trouble is, though the food is very good, the students are slightly too keen. You never get a full sentence out of your mouth without some pimply sixteen-year-old tucking your napkin in your neck like a barber and asking, 'Did you want more peas?'

As I might have expected, I was asked to 'sing for my supper'. Coco has a problem. The conversation went something like this . . .

(*Student*) 'Would you like to sit at this table, sir?'

(*Channel*) 'Yes, that'll do nicely.'

(*Student*) 'And you, sir?'

(*Me*) 'Well, I *am* having lunch with the Principal, Boggins.'

(*Student, pointing to the napkin before me*) 'Here's your napkin, sir.'

(*Channel — with a wry grin; he likes to see himself as a man with a sense of humour*) 'And this, boy, is your leg.'

(*Student, smiling nervously and backing away from Coco's outstretched hand*) 'I know, sir.'

This farce continued throughout ordering our meal. The boy was more formal than formality itself. By the time the food arrived Channel had gone through all his small talk and was arriving at the point he really wanted to discuss.

(*Channel*) 'Now look George, I know you're very loyal to old Spaight, well, we all are, but you especially since you've been his pupil and then worked with him for. . . .'

(*Student*) 'Carrots, sir?'

(*Channel*) 'Mmm' (nodding) '. . . years and years. . . .'

(*Student*) '"Mm", yes or "Mm", no, sir?'

(*Channel*) '"Mm", yes please.'

(*Student — to me*) 'Carrots, sir?'

(*Me*) '"Mm", yes please.'

(*Channel*) 'And I don't wish to force you away from that. . . .'

(*Student*) 'Peas?'

(*Channel*) 'Yes, please.'

(*Me*) 'Yes, please.'

(*Student*) 'I'm afraid peas don't come with *yourn*, I was only asking *him*.'

Coco reddened. He is definitely not 'him' to one of his students.

(*Channel*) '*Get him some peas.*'

The student went off in a huff. Coco resumed his story. It seems that Spite has sent in his resignation. Coco wants to accept it ('I don't want the poor man to suffer here') but he's worried as to what weight in law the resignation of a man not in possession of *mens rea* would have. But if the County failed to accept the resignation, was Spite not equally being hard-done-by?

'It's a sorry mess. It's only happened before with non-professional staff, so the legal advisers aren't sure what they should do. I believe they're scouring Local Authority Legal Departments up and down the land for. . . .'

'Gravy?' Our student was back.

'*Go away!*' Coco roared. The training restaurant hushed.

'But you haven't had any roast spuds, sir.' The student went away anyway.

'Look,' said Coco, 'What I was wondering was could we rely on you to carry on as HOD(Temp) on a sort of . . . indefinite basis?'

'Indefinite?'

'Till we have to make a decision about Spaight.' He leaned forward, dipping his tie in his lunch and lowering his voice, 'though frankly I believe we will be in a position to accept his decision once we're in a position where a decision *can* be made . . . and once of course we're in receipt of the decision of the Local Authority's Legal Officers as to whether his decision is acceptable and legally viable or not *as* a decision . . . am I clear?'

'Do you know G.E. Biggs, by any chance, Mr Channel?'

He scratched his head with his fork, then said, 'I taught him Maths years ago . . . doesn't he play cricket for the Old Boys?'

'That's the one,' I said. I wouldn't have been surprised if they'd turned out to be cousins.

'Anyway, don't worry about Biggs,' Coco said. 'He's all right, he works for a bank. Job for life . . . licence to print money, cheap mortgage, all that. What I'm suggesting to *you* is that, when the job comes to be advertised next year, the man who's been holding the fort for six months or so and making a good shot at it will have put himself in a pretty strong position, should he wish to apply for the job . . . get my drift?'

The table next to us was full of engineer-tutors. They couldn't hear Coco but we could hear them. Boggins, our student waiter, whipped the napkin from the neck of one of them and said, 'Anything for the week-end, sir?' which the engineers thought was hilarious. I thought Coco might explode . . . but he said nothing. Maybe he *does* have a sense of humour.

Wednesday 25th May
Though Coco went to great pains to impress the need for secrecy on me during our lunch, I *have* in fact talked over the matter of my extended temporary promotion with Elizabeth. It's only right, after all, between husband and wife.

Elizabeth seems to feel it's wrong of me to be out of sorts with NUT policy.

'Does the NUT have a policy on the matter?' I asked.

'I've no idea, George, but if they did I'm sure you'd be out of sorts with it if you played ball with Channel for too long.'

I don't know why I should give a fig for the NUT's policy . . . I belong to NATFHE. Whether *they* have a policy or not is impossible to tell — their bulletin board at college is smothered with odd bits of printed matter and erratically typed notices like:

'Doge for sail'
or
'Mem bers are rem minded that the summer terms bar-b-q is being held to raise funds fpr A frica.

Your sup ort is appreciated.

      (signed) Nev. Vincent. Br. Sec.'

I'm not insensitive to colleague's needs — some workplace solidarnosh never goes amiss. To be certain I didn't make any political gaffes I approached the young Vincent . . . an informal chat, I thought, just to confirm I wasn't encroaching on a firm rule of the union. I don't want my first task as HOD(Temp) (Temp Ext) to be coping with an industrial dispute.

I took him a cup of coffee in the Staff Coffee Lounge, settled next to him on an easy chair and said, 'Hullo, young Nev, how's the family then?'

'I'm not married, George.'

Not an auspicious start.

'Oh well, I said breezily, 'I was just passing the time.'

'Is it about the HOD(Temp)(Temp Ext) business, George?' he said.

It's just as well I was sitting down. Coco had said it was 'most secret, very private matter, not to be divulged at this delicate moment . . . negotiate from strength . . . etc. . . . '

'What about it?'

'You want to know where you'll stand with us.'

I was agog.

'Mm,' I said.

'Well, it's an extraordinary time here at Mugsborough. We are in extraordinary circumstances and extraordinary methods must be employed. I said to Coco, you've been here so long it must be your turn to be HOD whether that's proper HOD, HOD(Temp) or even HOD(Temp) (Temp Ext) . . . the last of which is a new one on me and seems to be a job Coco's invented specifically for you. Good luck to you, that's what I say.'

And he drank his coffee and left.

So *this* is how things will be with Coco. *This* is what it's like at the top table . . . all cut-and-thrust. Behind-the-back-ery. Deviousness. I am warned. What else can you expect from a silver-haired, silver-tongued smoothy who buys a new Terylene suit every month at Man-at-C&A? Could a man who shares coiffure with Bobby Charlton and Arthur Scargill be suitable for a College Principal? *This* is what you can expect from a man who keeps a spare electric razor in his desk in case the Chairman of the County Education Committee should call unexpectedly. I shall be wary.

*

8 p.m. Patel rang.

'I've just been speaking to Paul Peterson. He's had a few young chappies at the ground, seeing if they can get a roller out.'

'And?'

'He says it's no good. He says the outfield is like a jolly water-meadow. He says this weekend will have to be cancelled too.'

I don't know if I can stand it.

Tomorrow, as a sop to myself, I'll extend my lunch-hour, go into town. I'll have a lonely pint, I'll buy some tomato seedlings of a guaranteed English variety and also HIRE A LAWYER TO DEAL WITH THE PATIO DOORS.

Saturday 28th May
Has not been a very good day.

George Jolly lives in the road leading to our ground. He rang at 1.20 p.m.

'George, we've got a problem.'

Not another, I thought. A man can't be a thrusting young executive seven days a week.

'Go on,' I said wearily.

'Well, I've just seen a lot of chaps walking down our road with the cricket gear.'

'Good for them!' I said. 'Aren't they lucky!' There was an element of sarcasm in my tone. 'Do they know something I don't?'

'No,' George Jolly said in a voice like an undertaker presenting his account, 'you know something they don't.'

'*I* do?'

'You do. Our ground is the only one in this road . . . get it now?'

Disaster! We hadn't told the opposition about the cancellation. Dis-aster!

'Well, what stupid fool didn't ring them?'

'Our Hon. Sec.'

'But that's me!'

'Yes.'

Double disaster! Triple disaster! I had to think fast. I said, 'Is there any chance of the ground being playable?'

'I'll have a look.'

He didn't sound hopeful, but two minutes later he was back on the line.

'Yes . . . just. Are you going to tell them or try to get a team up?' he asked.

I tried to get a team up. Frantic phone calls followed, desperate pleading with players past and present (Elizabeth said I should go and dig a couple out of the churchyard). I crawled, wheedled, promised return favours and eventually came up with a team . . . well, nearly. Nine men.

When I arrived at our ground fifteen minutes later the sun was shining but the members of Mugsborough Publicans' Health and Exercise Club 2nd XI were not. They had changed — luckily George Jolly had the key to the changing rooms — but did not feel the presence of George Jolly alone was sufficient welcome. It's hard to blame them.

The team I'd gathered was so (not a batting order and I've included brief descriptions):

(1) George Jolly (fat)

(2) G.E. Biggs (fraternal delegate from the Karl Marx Youth League to OHCC — keen)

(3) Paul Peterson (much exercised at having his Saturday plans changed at short notice . . . also has discovered speck of dirt on his shirt)

(4) Patel (rolling eyes)

(5) G.V. Lyall — me (slightly flustered)

(6) George Long (a very out-of-form, out-of-condition ex-player of ours in his late forties . . . his attendance was a personal favour, as he kept telling me)

(7) George Long Junior (a thirteen-year-old schoolboy with arms and legs that seem slightly longer than his nerve endings; i.e. he kept falling over his own feet)

(8) A friend of Patel's whose name was unpronounceable but was close enough to 'Ranjitsinhji' to go into the scorebook as that. Biggs expressed the idea he might be a descendant . . . but it seems unlikely to me, unless ayahs are now instructing future Jam Sahibs in the Birmingham dialect.

(9) George Meredith (Christina's insurance salesman spouse. I simply went across the road, snatched the dishcloth from his hands and said, 'Come on George, we're going to play cricket.' 'Oh good,' he said, 'I've seen it on t.v. Will I be a batter or a bowler?' 'Batter, I should think, George.' Fish batter.)

And that was it; that was our team.

Albert turned up with his three-legged dog 'Patch' (bought cheap during the off-season on a Sunday trip to Club Row Market in London — 'the thing to do, George,' he said, 'is to wait about until the market's closing, then you can strike a really good deal'). Albert claims his dog is amazingly agile (considering his disability) and could field in the deep and return the ball faster by running with it in his teeth than many of our players could by throwing.

He may be right.

We tossed up and Mugsborough Publicans' H & EC 2nd XI put us in — a small concession designed to allow our 'stragglers to turn up', as the publicans' vice-captain confided to me. What a kind thought! Nice men.

George Jolly went and fetched two painters working on the house next door to his, thus giving us eleven men and freeing us of the spectre of Albert and his three-legged dog. A paint-spattered 'bib-and-braces' outfit isn't exactly 'whites' but we were hardly in a position to be fussy. They both had white sunhats, anyway. We sent Albert into town for some loaves of Mother's Pride, a huge tub of margarine, some ham and a couple of dozen Co-op jam tarts.

Paul Peterson and I opened. *He* claims I ran him out — but it's the non-receiver's job to call for a run on a leg-bye, surely, and the fact that he didn't forced *me* to do it all of a rush.

George Jolly came in number three and scored two quick runs during the next half-hour.

I was out for three off a ball that nipped back viciously from what had (until recently) been a muddy rut in the rugby pitch — now our track.

The writing was on the wall — the rest of our innings went in just as disastrous a fashion, except for Ranji, who scored ten before skying one, and one of the painters (they were both called George) who played and missed, hit a six, played and missed, hit another six, hit yet another six and was then bowled out by the first ball the bowler put on the stumps. Not much of a showing from Hacks. Tea was taken early. We were 49 all out.

The tea was odd. The liquid part of it was as tea should be — except that we had to put the milk in first on account of our spoons being with Mrs Knightly (she's the widow of one of our great players of past days and makes our teas at home matches in return for very little money but a great deal of thanks from us and a little conviviality from George Jolly, who runs her and the tea kit around in his Morris Minor). Mrs Knightly had been under the impression that we weren't playing today, hadn't come and so the knives, forks and spoons hadn't come too.

The sandwiches — prepared by Albert — were spectacular. Biggs was the first to notice.

'This sarni's a bit thick, innit?' he said. He was right too. The Mother's Pride in an ordinary sandwich can never be more than ¼-inch x 2 thick. The Polish ham was about 4 thou thick. But the whole sandwich was about 1¼ inches! The rest was made up of *Eezispred* marge.

I collared Albert.

'Marge go on all right, Albert?' I asked.

'Not bad.' He made out to be sharpening the scorer's biro.

'What do you make of this then?' I showed him Biggs' sandwich.

'Oh that was an early one . . . before I worked it out.'

'What out?'

He took my elbow and drew me to one side. His dog limped after us.

'I 'aven't got no *knife*.'

I looked at the offending ham sarni.

'Albert,' I said, 'this bread is carrying ¼-inch thick marge over most of its exposed surfaces. Now the fat got there somehow. How?'

Albert held up his dirty forefinger and waggled it. 'This.'

'*Oh Albert!*' I said. 'How *could* you?'

'Only a few,' he said, putting the finger in his mouth, sucking it and then looking closely at the result, 'till I found something else. Look at it from my point of view . . . there were no knives available, I was rushed off my feet, so I had to do the best I could.'

'What else did you find?' I said. Albert wouldn't look into my eyes.

'Just an implement,' he said.

I looked down. Albert's three-legged dog, Patch, was licking residual margarine from the surface of an old pink plastic cricketer's box which lay on the floor.

100

Biggs came to retrieve the sandwich. He pointed at the pink box the dog was licking.

'Isn't that the box I lost at Merryton last season . . . or was it the season before? What do you think of this rotten sandwich, George?'

I put my arm round his shoulders and said, 'I think you've probably had the best of things . . . you've probably got the nicest sarni in the room, Biggs.'

He obviously thought I was mad.

Albert diplomatically took his dog for a limp until our tea was over. The Co-op jam tarts, ancient as they were, went well. The ham sandwiches didn't go at all . . . but then they wouldn't. Biggs reclaimed his box. If he'd held the information I did he might have gone and bought a fresh one, or at least given it a jolly good scrub. If the other players held the information I did they'd probably want to give their throats a jolly good scrub.

Looking across the ground at Albert and his dog as they took their constitutional, I found it difficult to believe that such an eccentric man could ever have been entrusted with the well-being and education of children. I knew his face would have that wounded 'why-me?' look on it. His dog would fall over every time it tried to pee. Later, Albert will sidle up and tell me he's decided to forgive me for being so rude.

*

Fielding. Not our best ever showing in the fielding stakes, was this match. It all started in setting the field. Biggs was to open the bowling at one end, Paul Peterson at the other. George Jolly set the field; the painters at mid-off and mid-on, George Long and his son in the covers, myself at long leg, Ranji at deep square leg, Peterson at mid-wicket, Patel at backward square leg . . . old Jolly even came plodding down to join me on the long leg boundary. I think the opener must have had the distinct impression Biggs was going to play a leg side game.

He would have been wrong.

The first delivery was crashed over the head of mid-off for four. Biggs held his hand up.

'*Sorry* . . . sorry chaps.'

The second delivery was crashed over the head of mid-off for four.

'Getting my length.'

Then the fun started.

'Would you go back to the boundary, George?'

George Long and his son left their allotted places and marched to the boundary.

'Oh no, not *you*,' said Biggs.

But it was too late. *All* the Georges had marched to their respective boundaries . . . except for George Jolly and myself, of course. We were already at ours.

'No no. I meant George the painter,' Biggs called, 'the other George should come back.'

Of course he was facing the painters by then, so only they heard him clearly. *Both* of them came back to their places . . . mid-off and mid-on. Biggs knelt down, the non-receiving batsman offered to help him. While Biggs and the batsman conferred I noticed George Meredith standing on the boundary by my side in full wicketkeeper's regalia.

'What are you doing here?' I asked.

'*He* told me to come, your friend the bowler.'

Biggs stood up.

'Look,' he cried. 'I want everyone except George-the-painter-at-mid-off to come to their respective infield positions. George-the-painter-at-mid-off I want to go to the mid-off boundary.'

'Does that include us?' asked George Meredith. Biggs stared at his wicketkeeper.

'*Don't be stupid!*'

'Don't be stupid yes or no?'

'Yes yes. *Everyone come in* except George-the-painter-at-mid-off . . . he goes to the boundary. Everyone else *in*.'

George Jolly and I supposed we were included . . . we supposed Biggs knew what he was doing. We advanced. We supposed too much.

'*Not you!*' Biggs screamed. He almost woke Paul Peterson — who'd lain down — and his voice was sounding decidedly cracked. '*You go back!*'

'Who?' cried George Long.

'The two Georges.'

All the Georges went back to the boundary. Biggs knelt down again. The non-receiving batsman joined him, kneeling too. The receiver and the square leg umpire talked — they assured me after — of Wittgenstein and painting and poetry. The other umpire seemed to be asleep on his feet.

The non-receiving batsman called.

'Will just the George he wants go to the boundary and all the others go to the places they were in first of all.'

'But which George does he want and which of us are the others?' George Long called. We all nodded agreement.

The batsman went and stood next to mid-off, waving his bat.

'Only this one,' he called, 'all the other Georges go back to where you were and let's get on with the b*****y game.'

We all did as he asked . . . though it's a strange sight to have a field set by an opposing batsman, and a stranger one yet to have to watch your opening bowler finish his over between sobs.

Another mix-up occurred when we changed ends, this time with Paul Peterson orchestrating the Georges into something like a rugby scrum between the wickets.

'I want that George over there, and that George down there . . . no no . . . not *you*, I want *that* George. And those two Georges had better go down in front of the wicket. . . .'

It didn't take the opposition long to get the runs. In a way that was quite a relief because I think we were all beginning to tire of playing musical Georges. I suppose some small thanks must be offered that the opposition didn't open with one right-handed and one left-handed batsman — a common enough ploy — because we'd have been there all night. As it was they got the runs without losing a wicket.

*

I drove George Meredith home. The others went on to the pub but George was overwrought about missing his beloved Christina.

'We're very attached, you know,' he said.

Looking at him, with the thin moustache on his upper lip, his furtive grey eyes, his new all-polyester blazer and his Hush Puppy shoes it's difficult to envisage. It's hard to believe that Christina uses him as anything other than an unpaid hotelier . . . a man who provides the house and the money to run it, a man who washes up all the time, irons nightly, knows where the feather duster is kept, owns his own pinnie.

'I don't think she'd be that keen on me playing every week, George, I have to say. I did enjoy today's little outing, though.'

Ah well, if he enjoyed it, there's a ratio of 21:1.

Back at his house George and Christina proved me wrong about their relationship.

'Are you hurt?' she asked, burying his little head in her ample bosom, wrapping her arms about his ears, smothering his balding pate with kisses. 'Did you wear protective thingies all the time? Did they bowl fast at you?'

I left quietly, refusing an offer of coffee.

Back at home my welcoming committee showed a little more self-control.

'What are *you* doing here?' Elizabeth asked. She was wearing a piece of boldly printed green cloth, wound about herself in such a way as it covered the essentials. 'I thought you'd been playing cricket.'

'I have . . . see, my forehead is sunburned.'

I showed her. She said, 'But it's a bit inconvenient right now, George. We're rehearsing . . . I thought you'd go to the pub with your cronies. You always do.'

I was about to explain when a man came into the room wearing a band of ostrich feathers about his head, a piece of fake-leopard-skin about his hips and nothing else. Also he was carrying an *assegai*. He leaned on his spear and said, 'You must be George. I'm Tony Tremlet, but for the course of this production you can call me Nagogo Oomdoomer.'

I learned later it was spelt N'g'go M'dma, and was the name of the fictional Zulu chief in the play he's doing with Elizabeth. It seems they'd decided my cricketing was a good time to get together and go through their parts.

'I decided,' said Tony, 'that some of Elizabeth's lines need a thorough going-over with her. It's why she had her difficulties as Emma Hamilton last year.'

'I didn't know she played Emma Hamilton,' I said.

I wished I'd made Meredith walk home . . . or paid his cab

104

fare for him, or even taken up their half-hearted offer of coffee. When I abandoned George and Christina to their reunion, I'd hardly had sitting on my sofa and talking to a Zulu in mind as a game plan for the rest of the evening.

'She *didn't* play Emma Hamilton . . . that's just the point. If she's to move from backstage to stardom she'll have to get her parts word perfect.'

'Which parts?'

He adjusted his loin-cloth and said, 'Come on George. We're all men here.'

Some of Elizabeth's parts were pretty obvious under the boldly printed cloth she wore, and I thought that Tony Tremlet must have missed a vital conversation with his father during his teens to make a statement like his last.

'I'll make some coffee,' said Elizabeth (my male companion!). 'We could do with a break, anyway.'

'Not for me,' I said, 'I have to make a phone call to cancel tomorrow's match and then I'm off down The Dog and Bucket to wet my whistle.'

When I left the coffee was brewing and Elizabeth was squirming helplessly at the feet of the big butch N'g'go M'dma, he of the truly amazingly white skin and the Zulu grunts. He's an English teacher at E.'s school, I know. She's talked about him in the past.

I do sometimes wonder about the people in my profession.

Sunday 29th May

I intended to spend this morning spreading manure. When I told E. she said, 'Stick to the garden, eh?'

I went back to the colour supplement. How many *Sunday Times* readers can afford a new 'Seven' series BMW? None that I see in our local newsagents. New bicycle clips is their limit.

Later I made her ladyship's elevenses as a peace offering — though I'm not really sure how I've transgressed. I thought I'd show a bit of interest in her drama, cheer her up.

'Is he a good actor, that Tony?' I asked.

'Why do you bring him up?'

'Just wondering. What sort of Zulu is he meant to be?'

'A b****y warrior chief, and I'm his bride to be who's stolen by the Secret Police and raped . . . all right?'

'Convert, is he?' I said.

'Convert?'

'You know, like a Roman Catholic. After all, there can't be many white Zulus.'

'The trouble with you, George Lyall, is that you're uneducated and ineducable.' She sighed heavily. 'There's the world of difference between Naturalism and Realism.'

'Mm,' I said, 'perhaps I'll give Rudi Brathweight and Patel a ring, see if they can help you out. Add a bit of Realism.'

She threw her coffee cup. I fielded it well, though of course I couldn't field the coffee. That went up the kitchen wall. I can understand her anger; she probably never thought I knew so much of drama. Stanislavski isn't just a place near Warsaw to me . . . oh no. I know what they *do* there. Elizabeth thinks all knowledge of the plastic and performing arts is her province alone. She's wrong.

I put on my green wellies, went out and spread horse manure liberally on the rose beds.

Tony Tremlet is an Australian, too . . . which makes his Zulu chief even more ludicrous.

The green wellies would have been perfect to field in yesterday. What a day! Albert did give me one interesting piece of information, though. I mentioned that next week was the home match with Netherpopham (the away one is the traditional last of season game). Of course the subject of our mutual (well, mutual *what*? — hardly friend) Spite came up.

'It's an odd business, the way he dashed out and left them after being such a stalwart,' I said, 'I suppose he was simply embarrassed by the behaviour of Madeleine.'

Albert told me I couldn't be more wrong. It seems he'd stormed into a special AGM of the club and told them it was the groundsman, Nicholls, or him. They promptly voted against Spite. It seemed that Madeleine had had quite a few more 'friends' in the village than just the groundsman.

'She used to make special lemon-and-barley water in a stone jug and dispense it across the table in their back kitchen. I should imagine quite a few people in Netherpopham has a soft spot for such a kind lady.'

106

'How do you know all this?' I asked.

'The village postman told me. And the milkman. And the window cleaner. And the handyman. *And* the verger.'

'The *verger*?'

'He's their wicketkeeper.'

What gossip. I will find out more next week.

June

Philip Jenkins versus Netherpopham C.C.

Wednesday 1st June

It's no good making out there's no summer when June has arrived. The sun has at last got the message and we may look forward to playing the game and watching it played regularly . . . all under a scorching sky.

*

Lunchtime today I took myself off to a solicitor's office . . . Ableman, Ableman, Klapka and Ableman. My visit is part of a new resolve I've formed for the summer months — I will be *organised*.

It's only right and proper for a HOD(Temp)(Temp Ext) to be organised.

'Mr Thompson will see you now, Mr Lyall.'

Thompson sat behind his desk drinking PLJ and eating cottage cheese on ryebread.

'Lunch', he said by way of apology, 'I did warn you when you phoned.' He was referring to the fact that he'd made it clear when I made my appointment that he would miss his midday meal specially for me. The kindness of the legal profession passeth all understanding. I took my cue for informality from him.

'Sure, why not? Haven't got a spare one, have you?'

'Spare what?'

'Sandwich.'

'Certainly not.' He reached into a large plastic box on the chair by his side. 'I might have a spoonful of couscous. My wife keeps doing it.'

'Do any other solicitors work here?' I asked.

'Uh . . . Brickman, Lemmon, Miss Baxter and Miss Braine. The last two come in two days a week to do conveyancing only . . . aren't I what you wanted?'

'But no Ablemans?'

'No no. That's just the name . . . what exactly can we do for you?'

I told him the whole sorry story of P3W. He made sympathetic noises, then outlined a plan of action . . . private investigators, Companies House, letters flying back and forth, summonses, warrants, applications. It all sounded wonderful . . . for him.

'In the last analysis we could apply to have the company wound-up.'

'Would that mean I'd get my money?'

'Not necessarily.'

'But the man who owns it has an Audi Quattro. I've seen it parked outside their offices.'

'Have you seen the director driving it?'

'No, I've never clapped eyes on him . . . but it's obviously his car. Can't you have it repossessed until I get my lolly back?'

'No no, Mr Lyall. I cannot. That would be theft. We have a legal system which has to be gone through. . . .' And then he listed private investigators, Companies House, solicitor's letters, summonses, warrants, applications. I felt a certain sense of *déjà vu*.

'How much will all this cost?' I said.

'I couldn't say, Mr Lyall.' He had cottage cheese hanging

110

on his chin. Would I wish such a man to speak for me in court? Hardly.

'You must have some idea.'

'We're not plumbing contractors.' He rubbed his face with his hands. I presume this was meant to indicate he was amazingly over-tired, or perhaps that responsibility lay heavily on him. Thompson wanted to be seen as a man with gravitas, I knew, all the way down to his dark clothes, close-trimmed grey hair, heavy black briefcase and the sombre face that was now peering into it. Perhaps he had a set of tables hidden in the bag, and was even now calculating his possible fee. 'Or small builders.' He looked up. 'I don't suppose it would ever come to more than seven hundred.'

'Pounds?'

'*Of course.*' He was getting angry and he frowned. Since the cottage cheese had travelled to his eyebrow it made him look like Denis Healey, only less witty.

'Are you *sure* you're not a small builder? It would be cheaper to have the windows replaced.'

Thompson stood and said through clenched teeth, 'I'll have my secretary send you a bill.'

'What for?' I asked, incredulous.

'For *talking* to you.'

'And I'll get *my* secretary to send *you* one,' I said as a parting shot from the doorway. That floored him.

'What for?' he cried after me.

'*Listening.*' And I was through the door, down the stairs and into the street. God's own sunshine seemed to cleanse me after that unsavoury experience and I was glad to get back to my office and to my 'A'-levelled students, nervous staff and excited parents. I was glad to get back to the pure and unsullied business of writing references, snipping hours off part-time staff, telling three people they stand a good chance of getting one job.

Even Coco's palace intrigues are wholesome compared with a solicitor's daily business. To think my mother originally had it in mind for me to become one. If she could only see me now as HOD(Temp)(Temp Ext) I'm sure she'd be convinced I'd made the better choice.

Saturday 5th June

The Netherpopham home game. We have a lot of home games concentrated in this end of the season because we lose the last week of August and the first of September to Hack's RFC, who hold their trials, put up goal posts, black out alternate teeth to make themselves look more demonic . . . in fact do everything that rugger players need to do prior to kicking each others heads around for the next six months. During this late-summer RFC pre-season warm-up period OHCC becomes, in effect, a wandering side.

I've been worrying about this Netherpopham match. They're a bit of a pukka club, nobs and working men about half-and-half equally divided, and they have umpires, scorers, all that sort of thing. We Hack's players share the workload between us.

I wish we could make a better showing of the game's ancillaries . . . maybe one day we'll be a pukka club too. I mentioned it to Patel and he said, 'What does "pukka" mean?'

He's a wag, my little Indian friend.

'It's an Indian word,' I said, 'meaning "proper". I'd like us to be a proper club.'

'We are a proper club, George. If you want us to be proper in the Indian sense you'll have to lay on street beggars, starving thousands at the gate, a concrete track with coir matting on it and a pitch invasion whether we win or lose. Also half the team would have to go down with an amoeba in the gut on alternate weeks, thereby becoming unavailable.'

'But Netherpopham don't have all that,' I protested.

'Yes,' he said. 'And they're not a pukka club. The mere provision of umpires does not in itself give them the right to have airs and graces. We will share umpiring between ourselves as we have always done.' He paused. 'And this year we will beat them.'

We're at full strength this week, or as near as. Jenkins and Rudi Brathweight will open the bowling, Paul Peterson and Rudi the batting. We've included George Jolly to stop Peterson taking over the captaincy . . . Brian Cook is still abroad somewhere. Albert swears it's because of his building business going bust and him being chased by creditors. I don't believe it. Albert has an over-active imagination.

112

We didn't start very well. Netherpopham's openers (they won the toss) were quite classy and hammered a hundred off our bowlers in record time. It was the clapping for the hundred up that started Jenkins off. I was fielding at mid-off and I could hear him swearing as he came back to his mark. So could both batsmen. His next ball was wild and was called for four byes. When Jenkins next walked back to his mark he didn't swear. He didn't make any sound at all. His lips were pressed tightly together, his cheeks were purple, his eyes bulging. As he stormed down to the bowling crease I hardly dared watch.

The ball wasn't that quick, but the batsman was sufficiently put off by Phillip Jenkins' appearance to give an inside edge.

'Howsaaaargh!' screamed Jenkins. He had his arms extended, pointing past the umpire's ears; his nose was about four inches from the umpire's nose. He was doing his Denis Lillee impersonation again. Our wicketkeeper, young Butcher, held the ball safely in his hands. The umpire — provided by the opposition — slowly lifted his finger till it was right in front of his own and Jenkins' noses.

'Out.'

Jenkins was a very happy man. The batsman was not.

'I haven't got wooden pads, Dad!' he called as he departed.

'I'll see you later,' called his Dad.

The next man in was the verger; a stocky man in his forties, he had a placid, calm-looking face with grey hair that rose to a tonsure imposed by nature. It seemed wrong somehow for him to be dressed in white, he was more priestly than a priest. His fellow players clapped politely from the boundary. The verger held his bat in the air to acknowledge this, then said to Jenkins and the umpire, '*Ludus enim genuit trepidum certamen et iram, Ira truces inimicitias et funebre bellum!*'

'You may well say your prayers, cocker, you'll need 'em,' said Jenkins.

'Horace,' said the batsman.

'All right; you may well say your prayers, *Horace*, you'll need 'em.'

But the verger didn't 'need 'em'. He took a guard and then carted our bowlers all over the ground. We each had a go . . . Jenkins, Rudi, Biggs-and-his-gravity-defying-donkey-drop, Patel trying to wrist-spin on a track that was still a little damp from the winter and spring (when will it dry, September?). I even had a go with a slow-medium, straight-up-straight-down technique. Not a sausage. The fieldsmen spent more time looking for the ball in bushes than fielding it.

Netherpopham finally declared on 187 for one. Tea-time.

With our memories of Albert's tea, the return of Mrs Knightly was most welcome. Fluffy little angel cakes, wafer-thin slices of cucumber, strong tea allowed to stand for the right amount of time . . . that's the stuff of cricket teas, and the lady in question knows it. When I die I would like my cricket bat, *The Idea of History* (by R.G. Collingwood) and a dozen of Mrs Knightly's angel cakes buried with me. They should see me through the afterlife quite nicely . . . as long as I bump into another spirit with a ball to get up a match with — perhaps he might also have a copy of *Gibbon* he's willing to swap after the first few million years. He'll have to make his own tea arrangements, I'm afraid, till we trip upon some celestial Mrs Knightly.

A lady visitor who wasn't quite so heartily welcomed in all quarters was Madeleine Spaight. *I* for one didn't even know she was still in town.

'Hey, look. It's Maddy,' someone said, and there she was strolling towards the tea-room. Large as life. She had Carl Norton on her arm too.

'Hello fellows.' She waved and quickened her pace somewhat. The 'fellows' gathered like bees round a honey-pot. I pulled Norton to one side while the Netherpopham captain harried his team onto the field.

'What are you up to?'

'Up to?'

'That's Spite's wife.'

He shook his head.

'She hasn't been Spite's wife for twelve years. Anyway, I don't know what you mean, Lyall. I've just come along at Phillip Jenkins' invitation to introduce myself to Hack's.'

'Introduce?' I didn't understand at first. 'You mean play for us? Have you any experience? We're a good team.'

Just as I said it Rudi lapped a ball straight at square leg. The ball hit the fielder on the chest and fell into his hands. Netherpopham didn't even bother appealing . . . Rudi merely tucked his bat under his arm and marched towards us. Norton grinned and walked away.

*

As a team we didn't acquit ourselves badly. We were beaten twenty runs short of the target. Paul Peterson wanted to stick when we got to a hundred and twenty, but Jolly — who was at the crease — would have none of it. The last four wickets went down for forty-seven, but as George Jolly said, we are not in a league and we should therefore make a match of it wherever possible. 'I don't believe Cooky would have done that,' said Peterson. 'I believe he would have tried for a draw at this one, then gone on to win the one at the end of the season.'

No one answered. If young Peterson didn't know, how could you tell him?

George Jolly swears Brian Cook is languishing in a Spanish prison, and that it's just that element of gamesmanship in his personality which has landed him there.

'How do you know?' I asked.

'I just know. I've been around a lot longer than you, young George, and I've known Cooky since he was a kid scrumping at the bottom of our orchard. There's more to this than meets the eye.'

I had this mystery available to take my mind off my own anguish . . . a duck; I was bowled by a real snorter. After waiting so long for the season to start it seems *so unfair* to suffer as much bad luck as I have.

We all went to The King Henry's Goose to drown our sorrows. Quite a party developed. Madeleine took it in turns to sit on the laps of members of both teams and flirt with them . . . harmless really, though she does weigh a bit. Of course it could be guaranteed that when she came to our table she'd plonk herself on me (I haven't forgotten that incident in the hotel) and it could also be guaranteed that, just as she did so, George and Christina Meredith would come in.

'My,' said Christina, 'aren't we seeing a new side of George? You *have* got your hands full. I should get her off if I were you, though . . . Elizabeth's just parking the car.'

Good advice. I don't suppose the ex-Mrs Spaight has been unloaded so fast in her life . . . I dumped her on Patel, who almost disappeared under her, then I headed for the bar and bought the quick-witted Christina a drink. She deserved it. Elizabeth came in with M'pop N'gogo, or whatever his name is. I was relieved to see they were wearing all their clothes . . . I don't think I could have stood the ribbing I'd have got from the lads if they'd come in their African drag.

'Hullo George . . . win?' said E., kissing me.

'No.'

'Oh . . . never mind. Score many runs?'

'No.'

'Oh . . . never mind. Take any wickets?'

'No.'

The white Zulu slapped me on the shoulder.

'Don't take any notice of her, sport. Cricket can be a funny cookie to crumble.'

'*Cookie to crumble*?' I said. This man teaches English!

'That's right, mate. A hard nut to grind.'

I looked at his bland, stupid expression, at the orange ring of make-up left on his neck. I looked into his eyes.

'How did the dress rehearsal go?' I asked.

'Not bad.' He was pleased with himself.

'Who won?' I said, and walked away before he had a chance to answer. A funny cookie to crumble indeed.

Sunday 6th June

Mugsborough Police. A feeble side really, and we must consider ourselves suckers-up-to-authority for keeping the fixture on. Jolly won the toss and put them in — an attempt to make some sort of game of it. They were all out for 88. Peterson and Patel knocked off the runs in next to no time. I didn't even get a look-in, which makes me so far this year . . . 'three', 'nought', and 'did not bat'.

Things wouldn't be so bad if the imminent arrival of the Exam Reaper did not mean I have to drop out for the next couple of weeks. My three match average is one-point-five, not much cop for a specialist batsman. If I could I would play on and try to improve it, I'm sure things will pick up, but my workload at the beginning of the 'A'-level season is truly horrendous. The nearest I'll get to cricket is watching bits of the World Cup on t.v., not much of a prospect, really, for the serious player.

Monday 7th June
A hard work day. Into my office, furious reading of papers, signing of documents. Meetings, organisation, etc., etc., etc.

E. rang before lunch.

'You haven't forgotten *The Second Rorke's Drift*, have you?' she said.

'Rorke's Drift? Where all those taffs were killed?'

'Yes, *The Second Rorke's Drift* is our play and we're opening tonight and you're coming to see it.'

At least we'd established *The Second Rorke's Drift* wasn't the Yorks/Glamorgan match going on (even as I write) in Middlesbrough.

'I'm afraid I'm too busy for that, Elizabeth.'

'Does that mean you've got a date?'

'Certainly not.'

'Meet me at the stage door, then, Johnny.'

Johnny who?

I twisted Patel's arm, figuratively speaking, and we presented ourselves at the Mugsborough Playhouse at seven-thirty sharp.

I'm afraid we hopped the wag after the first act . . . I can only watch torture, beating, rape, suicide and murder in limited sessions. I left a note for my wife with a greasy-haired boy in black clothes at the back of the theatre: '*Urgent committee meeting called. Have had to confer with Patel. Meet me in Henry's Goose. Love George.*'

When E. and her fellow players presented themselves at about ten p.m., they were rapturous. For the first time ever, it seems, *The Second Rorke's Drift* had played to an audience larger than the cast.

'I'm thinking of turning professional,' M'boto U'pupu, otherwise known as Tony Tremlet, said.

'Professional what?' said my little Indian friend before I had a chance to stop him.

'Actor. I love being in rowel.'

'Rowel?' I said.

'*Acting*. With your lovely wife as my leading lady I could storm the fringe.'

'You are going to have a haircut?' said Patel, in an accent that made him sound like a minor civil servant in Calcutta.

M'gumba J'ambutty leaned across to Elizabeth and said, 'I think your husband's mate's a bit slow on the uptake.'

E. broke off from the girl she was talking to and said, 'Oh no. He is definitely not.'

'I think he is, said Tony Tremlet back in his day-to-day Australian persona again, 'either that or the little b****r's a bit touched. It's only my personal commitment to his race and to downtrodden people all over the world that keeps me in conversation with him.'

It was then that the fight started. I never knew Patel could have such a temper. He pulled the Australian's hair and bit his cheek. A bearded Mancunian who'd played an Afrikaaner policeman with varying degrees of success tried to restrain Patel, but he bit him too. The Aussie took a swing and hit the Mancunian, who grabbed him. The Mancunian's girlfriend hit the Aussie while her Mancunian boyfriend held him. Patel bit the girlfriend. Tony Tremlet began pulling the Mancunian's beard as hard as he could.

I took my wife's arm and we left by a side door. I could hear two-tone sirens in the distance and, as I let the door swing shut, I could see the fight had warmed up considerably.

At home we had a large scotch each and I made Elizabeth promise to catch a diplomatic cold for tomorrow night's performance. She didn't take much convincing.

Tuesday 8th June

Went this evening to visit Patel on the picket line. He has mounted a one man patrol outside the Mugsborough Playhouse and is wearing a sandwich board knocked-up for him by a sympathetic West Indian carpenter. The front of the board reads 'No to Racism in Mugsborough' and the back reads 'Condescension is Condemnation, Close this Play'.

He was holding a conversation with the local bobby, who

seemed a bit confused by it all. Not surprising, really. The same man batted number eight for the Mugsborough Police against us Hacks last Sunday, and on that occasion seemed a bit confused about which foot went in front of the other.

When the bobby left (walking very slowly and frowning lest some obstruction — the kerb? — took him all unawares) I sidled up to my friend and said, 'Did they arrest you?'

'No.' He thrust a pamphlet into a woman's hand. 'But it was no thanks to you, George. Fancy leaving me in a fix like that.'

'I didn't mean to. . . . I had Elizabeth there . . . you shouldn't have started it.'

'That Australian nitwit shouldn't have behaved like he did. Did I hurt him?'

'Elizabeth says he looks like he's got a love-bite on his cheek. Are you okay?'

'I'm perfectly well, George . . . *no racism in Mugsborough, Madam! I wouldn't buy tickets for this racist play if I were you!*' And he strode away.

Wednesday 9th June
Red letter day . . . the Prudential Cup starts. I did think about going to Swansea to see Pakistan play a team Richie Benaud calls 'Sroy Lenker', but of course the same responsibilities that have put the kibosh on my own active cricket for the next couple of weeks rule that out.

I was surprised on my way home from work to see Patel still doing his placard act. The bus stopped outside the Playhouse so I hopped off and said hello.

'Much doing?' I asked.

'Same as yesterday. They aren't selling tickets to the wretched play anyway. I'm just making sure it gets killed right off . . . you?'

'Not bad.' I noticed he had a tranny plugged into his ear. 'How's India doing?'

He scowled.

'Terrible. It's been raining . . . they're extending play till tomorrow.'

'Patel,' I said, 'I wonder if I might have a word with you about the play.'

He held his hand up, palm towards me, and said, 'I might have guessed, eh? You've been sent to talk me round. Well it won't work. I won't talk about it.'

'Let me talk about the picket then.'

'No.'

'You're wasting your time,' I said.

He shook his head slowly and backed away from me.

'You of all people, George. *You*. I thought *you'd* have understood.'

'The play's finished. . . .'

'You're too right it is. I've been writing to my cousins all over . . . England, Canada, Kenya, India. We will *all* picket.'

The fire of the fanatic burned in his eyes; how easily it is awoken in the most placid of us. It's just a question of finding the right trigger.

'The play was only on for two days, old chum. *You're* picketing *Oklahoma!* by the Mugsborough Amateur Musical Society.'

'Oh.'

He dropped the placard and scarpered. I didn't want to walk home with it under my arm, so I stopped a boy of about nine or ten and gave him fifty pence to carry on picketing for the next hour . . . I don't like musicals anyway.

I spent the evening reading a proposed syllabus for Geography . . . or rather I spent the first part of the evening trying to read it and the second part of the evening trying to think up some sensible criticisms to pencil in the margin. This is an Augean shovelful for a man with my talents in the geography department, aided as I was only by a *Phillips School Atlas* circa 1957 and my own vague recollections of cols, isthmuses and peninsulas. I am afraid our Geography lecturer will not think much of me.

I suppose I could always redeem myself by offering proposed exam questions on the syllabus. . . .

1. *Which countries are full members of the International Cricket Conference?*

2. *Where are they?*

3. *What sort of stone wall would you expect to find in Headingley?*

120

4. *See if you can recognise the following places from Richie Benaud's vocabulary*:

   a) Sroy Lenker

   b) g'dey frem dewn here et the Oevel

   c) Bredgteyn Berbeyduss

5. *Is the 'Mound'*:

   a) a place in Australia?

   b) a place in Australia full of drunken yobs?

   c) a heap of horse manure?

   d) a place in Australia full of drunken yobs shouting and throwing beercans?

   e) None of the above?

   f) All of the above?

6. *Which is the most important West Indian export cash crop*:

   a) sugar cane?

   b) sugar beet?

   c) fast bowling?

   d) marijuana?

. . . what fun . . . I could think these up for hours. It won't get the reports read and the lies written, unfortunately. I must knuckle down to HOD-type tasks.

Monday 20th June

I've had two full weeks of paperwork — weekdays and weekends both. Last weekend was away matches for Hacks . . . GCHQ Minders on Saturday, Bristol Lightermen's Recreational XI on Sunday. We won both matches while I wasn't there . . . just my luck. Norton played against the Lightermen (I need hardly say that not only is there no lighterman amongst them but few enough of them even live in Bristol) and George Jolly phoned on Sunday night to thank me for introducing him to the club and to say how nice it is to have a left-hander available who can bat high in the order and what a marvellous chap he was and . . .

'I didn't introduce Norton,' I said. 'Jenkins did.'

'But doesn't he work for you?' Jolly asked.

'We're barely on speaking terms. I don't like his little game with Maddy Spaight.'

'Oh, George . . . don't be a prude. He's a good bat.'

121

He may well be a good bat, but I don't think I'm being prudish. Cricket appears to be the last game in the world with some standards, and I don't see why we should contribute to their lowering.

Patel rang too. He'd trekked across England to watch his beloved Indians play Zimbabwe at Tunbridge Wells. I think he was as surprised as anyone to find himself watching one of the all-time great one-day games. He went on for about half an hour, giving me a ball-by-ball account of Kapil Dev's innings (all 175 runs!) Eventually I interrupted and said, 'The whole point of my neither playing nor watching cricket for the last two weekends is so I can work, my friend. If I allow you to go on much longer I'll soon get to a position where it would have been quicker for me to have gone and watched.'

'Don't you want to know?'

'*No*!'

Got it at last!

'I think you're being something of a spoilsport, George. There's something very sour about you since you've had the extra responsibility in your job.'

'Good night Patel. I'll call you during the. . . .'

The phone clicked. And he had the cheek to call me 'sour'. At least England beat Sroy Lenker today, or I'd never have got him off the line. Small mercies.

*

9 p.m. Today is the traditional start of the 'I want an expensive holiday' campaign from Elizabeth. She books late so she can claim to be saving money. The first move — established over the years — is to tell me that she hopes I won't be disappointed if she doesn't come on tour with me.

'I hope you won't be too disappointed, George darling, if I don't offer to come and score for your cricket team during this year's tour.'

This from a woman who thinks a slow bowler is one who takes a long time to get up to the crease!

Normally she then mentions some exotic location and the name of the friend she's going with — Christina for the last few years.

'Christina Meredith wants to go to Corfu this summer.'

A brief silence while she serves supper; carrot salad — bikini fodder — for her; porterhouse steak — mug's fodder — for me. She says, 'I thought we'd have some wine with it tonight . . . what d'you say?'

I say yes.

'She mentioned that I might go with her.'

'How much?' the condemned man asks.

'Seven hundred and fifty pounds.'

'Stone me!' This is the beginning of my ploy.

'Well, *that's* if we stay in the hotel and have window seats on the scheduled plane. We can have a self-catering villa with a maid that comes in and travel by charter . . . that's five hundred, if you include an allowance for meals and service.'

'Each?' I feign astonishment.

'No one's asking *you* to pay, George. How much is your hotel bill going to be in Little-Lumpton-on-Sea?'

This is where the poker-player puts his cards down . . . a royal flush.

'We're not staying in the hotel this year. Patel's getting us a tent.'

E. rolls her eyes and fetches more wine from the fridge.

'George, you can't be serious! A tent?'

I'm not, of course, serious . . . I am as fed up as Patel is with the establishment in Little-Lumpton-on-Sea. After an hour's hard bargaining we settle that Elizabeth and Christina can go to Minorca — not Corfu — and stay in a decent class of place and travel by scheduled craft rather than flying-pig-bin. For my part of the settlement we have arranged that Patel and I will leave the main party for this tour and settle ourselves in a place in Worthing that's got hot and cold running chambermaids and which offers something a bit more sophisticated in the breakfast stakes than 'egg, bacon, toast, marmalade and tea. All residents to note breakfast is not served after nine a.m.'.

I'm rather pleased . . . a painless success.

Tuesday 21st June
6.30 p.m. Patel rang.

'I just wanted to tell you, my fair-weather friend, that I've sorted us out, got us booked, all that.'

I was puzzled.

'You mean the tour?'

'Yes.'

'Have you been talking to Elizabeth?'

'No. I'm afraid we won't have facilities for her.'

'What are you talking about?'

'What do you think? The tent. I've booked it. Paid for it . . . using, I might add, a cheque drawn on my own personal bank account.'

I was aghast. I couldn't bring myself to say anything.

'George, George . . . are you all right?'

No neatly segmented grapefruits. No breakfast after nine. No sophisticated chatter in the bar all evening. *We* weren't even going to be in the jumped-up guest-house with the hoi polloi . . . *we* would be in a tent!

'No,' I said, 'I'm not all right.'

'I think you must be working yourself into the ground, you know. Why don't you come round and watch my video of India beating Australia yesterday?'

It's not my idea of a laugh to spend an evening watching Aussie bowlers getting no-balled at Chelmsford and I said so.

'I'll see you at the team selection meeting on Thursday.' I said. 'And we'll talk this tent lark over.'

'Maybe.'

Saturday 25th June

The reason for Patel's 'maybe' is to do with his large family and their extensive contacts. He has a cousin in Devon — a tobacconist — who puts him in touch with his son (the cousin's) who has a friend who's West Indian. The West Indian went to school with a chap in Kingston, Jamaica who's married to a girl named Joan from Edmonton. They have a son called Tommy and he's on the ground staff at Lord's.

Or maybe his friend is.

Anyway, the upshot of all that is that my friend Patel was

on the early train to London to go with the West Indian (who's name I forget) to use the tickets procured by Tommy for his mum, Joan, and his dad who's from Kingston, Jamaica (and whose name I also forget . . . or did I never know it?). Tommy's parents don't want the tickets because they've argued about how much Carlsberg Special to take, and eventually called the whole thing off. The West Indian friend of Patel's cousin's son is the one Patel is on the early train with. The reason Patel's cousin doesn't want to go is that he's too old. The cousin's son doesn't want to go because he doesn't like cricket . . . perhaps he comes from somewhere hilly.

Patel turned up for the team selection meeting on Thursday . . . but only to tell us we're not to have his services this weekend.

Lucky old Patel.

The rest of us have to content ourselves with the playing fields of Mugsborough and transistor radios. I have to admit, of course, that I'd rather play than watch. In fact I've had to admit that to Patel several times since he put his reason for unavailability to us . . . otherwise he'd have become unbearably smug.

Today we played South Bristol IS at home. They're a young team — except for a middle-aged captain. It's a fixture we picked up from a conference game three years ago . . . in fact they fill the gap left by the missing return match with the now-defunct David Ben Gurion Memorial XI (Secular Wing).

A sunny day and a good match was enjoyed by everyone . . . though there were a few strange features. One was that South Bristol IS had brought a twelfth man. This is no bad thing in itself since only ten of their chosen players turned up. The twelfth man changed and prepared to play.

South Bristol IS won the toss and chose to bat. Their twelfth man — being a specialist in no other role than being twelfth man — was put at number eleven in their batting order (I know all this because I have it from their captain). We contained them well, they were on one-forty or thereabouts when they were on their second-to-last wicket. The twelfth man was keen . . . he'd kept the telegraph going all afternoon, had been padded-up since the fall of the third wicket and was just about to have his moment of glory. Then a chap sat in the chair by his side and padded-up too. It was the missing player, arrived late.

'Hey! What's your game?' twelfth man cried. We heard that on the field. The missing player continued to put on his pads.

Twelfth man grapped the buckle from his rival's hand.

'I said what do you think you're up to? *I'm* batting.'

'Don't be stupid,' said the other fellow, 'you *can't* bat . . . anyway, *I* was picked. *You're* just twelfth man.'

'If you think being picked is so important, you should take care to show up on time. You're too late. *I'm* batting.'

The wicket fell. I think if I'd been South Bristol IS's captain I'd have declared at once and settled the matter of who became the eleventh *fielder* by the toss of a coin. He didn't though. He let them go on. The row became a fracas, then spilled onto the field. Both men took a bat, both men strode to the striker's end, both men called for a guard. They were left- and right-handed (the late-comer and twelfth man respectively), so there wasn't too much jostling . . . though the umpire was very perplexed.

'Ooh. I don't think we can have this . . . No. I don't think we can have this at all,' he said. 'Ooh no.' Since he was an umpire *they'd* brought, we were all rather depending on him to have had some previous experience of such odd behaviour.

The South Bristol IS vice-captain was batting at the non-striking end, and he solved the problem by coming down the wicket and kicking the late-comer very hard on the patella, then telling the twelfth man he should be a runner for the injured batsman. The South Bristol IS vice-captain was a chubby young man with bright red cheeks and he didn't look to me, frankly, as if there were such depths to his character. He may yet make a career in the diplomatic corps.

We made the runs, which made it three wins on the trot. Some of our batsmen did rather well . . . especially young Carl Norton with forty and Paul Peterson with fifty-five in as many minutes. I had complained to George Jolly about not getting a knock for a few weeks so he asked me to open. South Bristol IS opened the bowling with their captain, a dithering mousey little man in his fifties who bowled straight-up-straight-down balls that seemed to bounce about four times before they came on to the bat. I went down the wicket to the fifth ball — having just taken a two — and smothered it. I was two or three paces from my crease.

'How's that?' said the captain quietly as he walked back to his mark. The umpire (theirs) looked at me for a long time and then raised his finger. I couldn't believe it. Where I'd met it, he couldn't even have been sure that the ball would have reached the crease, let alone hit the wicket.

I didn't show dissent. It's not my style. I did tuck the orange juice away, though, so that if they called for drinks they should only have water.

They didn't call for drinks.

Today is June the twenty-fifth and my record stands as . . . 'three', 'nought', 'did not bat' and 'two'. I will not let the pressure get to me.

The second strange feature of our day (third if you include my unbelievable l.b.w.) was Brian Cook's wife, Jennifer. She came along at the end of the match, just as I was collecting boundary boards.

'Hello, George,' she called, 'long time no see.'

I can't carry more than four boundary boards without getting into all sorts of trouble with them . . . with five I have to juggle them back to the shed, six and I drop the lot. No one had been helping on this occasion . . . they'd all dashed off to celebrate . . . and I had something like ten boards hanging on to various parts of my anatomy. I must have looked like a shuffling woodpile.

'Hello, Jenny, I'm surprised you recognised me under this lot.'

'Always know you. I'll lock the car and help you over with them.'

In fact we dumped four boards, took three each and linked arms to walk back. She's an old friend and it's a long time since I'd seen her.

'How's that missing Brian?' I said. 'Still in Spain?'

''fraid so. It's as bad as being a cricket widow. Still there are compensations.'

'Like what?'

'Oh . . . peace and quiet. Independence. The use of our nice new car all the time . . . Brian's even signing the business over to me.'

She *is* pretty. And good-natured too. I like Jennifer. The sun was just dipping behind the trees, the evening air was warm, the perfume of stock was in the air . . . lovely. A bird called (I'm no good at recognising birds by calls or otherwise — let's just say it was neither a sparrow nor an eagle).

'What's your nice new car?' I said.

Summer evenings . . . wonderful. Jennifer's honey-coloured hair . . . a man can suffer grievous temptation. I am strong, though.

'An Audi Quattro . . . that one. It's smashing,' she said.

'They are nice aren't they? I'd love one,' I said. 'Do you know, the swine who put our leaky double-glazing in owns one . . . bought with *my* five hundred pounds!'

Perhaps I should have resisted the garlic sausage for lunch . . . she wouldn't speak to me for the rest of the evening, that's for sure. I was mystified and hurt. She didn't even talk to Elizabeth when she drove down to join us Hacks in the Henry's Goose. And Elizabeth went to school with her!

I wonder if we've committed some awful social gaffe? E. can be very blunt from time to time. I'm sure it's not me, anyway . . . I've been over and over my conversations with Jennifer. Unless, of course, she spied some unworthy thought in me: so full of artless jealousy is guilt it spills itself in fearing to be spilt.

Don't talk to *me* about the theatre. I've been there.

Sunday 26th June

Spent the morning watching a thunderstorm circling Mugsborough. No rain fell. Drove to the ground, distributed contents of club bag, put out boundary boards, turned on water-heater for showers, put American Cloth cover on tea-table, changed, did my warming-up exercises. No rain fell. Did the usual Sunday routine of jokes about missing lunchtime in the pub: 'If it's called off at two o'clock there'll be hell to pay, you know.' Still no rain fell. Took light roller out before captain inspected pitch. Everyone looked up at sky and said they didn't like the look of it. 'What's in a sky?' I said, trying to cheer them. Tossed up, we won, Peterson and myself were to open. Padded-up. Walked out to applause.

Still no rain. Waited around while umpire sought his missing counting stone (why does it have to be a *particular* counting stone?), then waited around while opposition field was set. Asked Peterson's opinion of that dirty big black cloud above us.

'Looks like it'll go round, George. We'll be okay,' he said.

Still no rain.

Took a guard, nodded that I was indeed ready, bowler started his run.

Then the skies opened.

So much for Sunday.

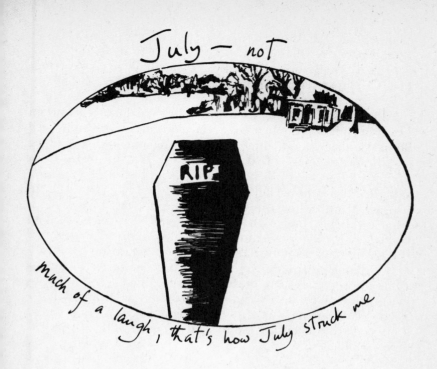

July — not much of a laugh, that's how July struck me

Sunday 3rd July

Saturday represented an unfilled gap in our calendar. The absence of Brian Cook and his network of friends and acquaintances means we've been at sixes and sevens to fill the gaps in our programme. Usually we don't bother much with the conference — old Cooky just rustles up some long-lost pals from a corner of Somerset. We've a gap in another couple of weeks, though, and I will have to organise something through the official system. If it's not all laid on, we'll have to go through the same boring arguments as last year (and the year before and the year before) as to whether we sign up with a league and thereby do away with mid-season gaps once and for all.

I don't really see us as a league side; scratching away at the last knockings to see whether we can just get a draw or not, refusing to speak to catch-droppers in the bar afterwards, pocket calculators concealed in our jocks, all that nonsense. We're a fun club.

Today, though, is one of our prime fixtures . . . the Bellow's Bank match. We'd all very much like to win it.

What a lovely day. Blue sky, unspecified birds tweeting, Ford Cortina starts first time, Ray Coniff on the car radio. . . .

Perfect.

Picked up Patel. He spent the whole of last weekend in London acting the larrakin, thereby missing the North Somerset flash-flood which only hit Mugsborough and three surrounding towns. He'd done untold damage to his grey matter by liberal applications of Carlsberg Special, Genuine Jamaica Rum and herbal cigarettes. When I went to pick him up last Monday for the 'net' we'd agreed on (to work out what's going wrong with my batting technique) he looked positively ill. Even this morning he looked pretty rough — a full seven days after India's magnificent win at HQ.

We drove north through rolling green fields. Gracious stone houses sat resting in the sunshine, like Georgian ladies who had gone for a stroll and, exhausted now, flopped at the kerbside awaiting supplies of cream cakes. Some ducks scattered from a village pond as we passed. The rustic life. Bucolic bliss.

Perfect.

Bellow's ground. A mock-Tudor clubhouse, changing rooms tucked at the back, well-stocked bar above, club room at the front, dining room to one side. Leather armchairs, polite employees, a highly polished wooden floor. A peek through the tall dark-oak and glass doors to the dining room reveals smoked-salmon mousse made in moulds, silver-foil covering cucumber sandwiches, a row of individual china tea pots — none of that queue-up-at-the-urn-Ern here! And is that a couple of jolly old champers buckets I spy in the corner? Yes, of course . . . we *know* it is.

Perfect.

The team arrives on time (no Norton today, we don't feed smoked-salmon mousse to Johnny-come-latelies). Everyone has brought their proper kit, there's no unseemly scuffle for cloakroom hooks, just as we know there will be no unseemly scuffle for places in the batting order. Everyone's on his best behaviour today. We have brought a twelfth man (George Long's teenage son, George) who can lug orange juice about, keep our scorebook up, be polite to the Bellow's people, all that. Rudi Brathweight has even offered to lend the boy a cravat!

Perfect.

Albert has been convinced to kennel Patch with a neighbour for the day. He is keeping his hands in his pockets and has promised not to try to help the Bellow's players in any way at all and especially not to do any of the Bellow's Bank senior management any favours by way of selling them something or by way of buying something on their joint behalves.

Perfect.

We were to bat first. I was in the middle order, so I sorted out a pair of pads, then took a deck chair and sat in the sun with the Sunday papers. I was happy. Warm, comfortable, with a glass of lemonade to drink and a newspaper to read. With a restful snooze for now, some cricket to watch and the prospect of a bit of batting before me. Later I would field like a demon, throwing myself about, rolling on the turf safe in the knowledge that there would be no dog's doings to dodge. I'd take a hot bath . . . no, I'd shower. *No*, take a hot bath *and* shower, then stroll into the dining room to eat a hearty cordon bleu supper given to me gratis by Bellow's Bank and by Terrison, their director and ex-Hack.

Perfect.

What do you get from a bank for nothing, normally, eh? Nothing, that's what. *We* were about to get the works.

Perfect.

I could drink (after my hearty supper) with impunity. Patel had drawn the short straw as far as driving goes . . . the only reason we'd even come in my car was that Mrs Patel needs their Toyota to take the little Patelettes to the Sunday afternoon Hindi class. Or was it Urdu? I daren't ask him which lot he is exactly for fear of provoking another 'Tony Tremlet Incident'.

The point is that Patel was obliged to chauffeur me home.

Perfect.

When I went to the crease we were in trouble . . . 30 for 3. Patel was already there on four and I had to face up to one of Bellow's chief clerks, a wily spinner in his fifties who could teach lessons to anyone about line and length. I decided 'application' was the order of the day. The Bellow's players are winners . . . anything other than outright victory is a defeat to them. I decided to make them work for it. I smothered the chief clerk for an over, then a medium-pacer was brought on. Patel took a single off him and then . . . and then I don't know what happened.

I had taken no alcohol, had no reason to be confident. Perhaps it was the day, the buzz of flies, the trickle of sweat on my forehead, the taste of the dust that had come up from the track. Perhaps it was the idea that my club needed me. Who'll know? Perhaps it was the polite crowd on the steps of the pavilion. Perhaps I was angered by the short fielders gathered round me, as if their rotten medium-pacer was I. T. Botham or something.

The medium-pacer ran down to the crease. I discovered an imaginary fly before my face. I waved, stood up. The umpire held his arm out. The bowler screeched (or so it seemed) to a halt, muttered something to Patel and the umpire, then went back to his mark. He ran down again. I stood again. The umpire put his arm out again, the bowler stopped again.

'I'm sorry!' I called. 'It's a wasp or something.'

The bowler turned beetroot. His captain came over and they had a long conversation with the umpire while the wicketkeeper, slips and short-fielders hunted around me for my imaginary wasp. How immoral of me!

'Are you all right now, bat?' called the umpire, testily.

At my end of the wicket we hunted the wasp for a few seconds more, then I said I was okay but could I take another mark? Only the wicketkeeper has trodden on mine. I managed to take up another couple of minutes like that, then the medium pacer served up a long hop which I crashed through the covers (if I say it myself and if I steal the phrase from Test Match Special) for four. I let the third go by, took two off his fourth ball and another four off the fifth, sending the close fielders scurrying off. Then Patel and I ran a desperately quick leg-bye, sliding home all flying caps, grounded bats and lungs full of dust. The crowd on the pavilion steps cheered. I waved my bat in recognition.

The spinner came back. I went down the wicket to him, head down, bat following right through, a four over mid-off . . . slightly mis-hit, it was meant to go over mid-on. No one except me knew, of course. The slowy sent down a full toss, hanging temptingly in the air for what seemed like an age. I had none of it, simply let it drop, then dug it out. There were a lot of fielders standing round with their hands in front of their faces for that one. He sent down another. I hit four along the ground. The crowd on the pavilion steps cheered again. This was the stuff . . . this was what I wanted, this was what I netted in the winter for. What I had to do was exercise some self-control. Not get too excited. I could do it . . . I'd done it before. He bowled again. I padded up outside my leg stump and ran one off it.

It was then I saw the Toyota. While the field was re-arranging itself for Patel (he's left-handed) I called him down the wicket and said, 'That dusty old Toyota's just like yours, Patel.'

We stood there with Bellow's players running past us.

We stared at it.

'It *is* mine,' he said.

They say that when you're drowning all your life goes before you. I think it's probably true. I certainly felt each ball of that wonderful innings. I felt it come on to the bat, I felt it leave me. I watched it fly to the boundary. All these hits, all these balls delivered, all these cheers and hopes of glory were in my mind as the Toyota wheezed to a halt. At first I'd thought . . . 'poor old Patel, fancy his family turning up and spoiling his match'. Probably one of the kids gone down with Montezuma's Revenge, or some ageing relative in Walsall has precipitated a family crisis by making an arranged marriage with a beautiful fourteen-year-old from Delhi.

Then I saw that it was Elizabeth driving.

'That's your wife,' said Patel.

The home side were waiting to re-start.

Elizabeth jumped out and waved her scarf.

'And that's her mother in the passenger seat,' said Patel. What a Job's Comforter he is!

Elizabeth waved more urgently.

'Ooo-ooh! Ge-yorge! Come *quickly*! We ne-*eed* you!'

'Oh no they don't,' I said.

Elizabeth began to advance. Her mother left the car too. I ran from the crease.

'Retired hurt,' Patel said. 'Indifferent meat curry last night, hurry-ups this afternoon. It's a common complaint.'

The Bellow's players nodded understandingly as I left the field of play. I went and hid behind the mock-Tudor clubhouse. I could hear Elizabeth talking to George Jolly, who was padding up. Then they began to search the building.

I went into the 'Away' dressing-room, tipped the stuff out of our bag, and got young Tommy Butcher, our wicket-keeper, to pile it all on top of me again.

'Are you sure, George?' he said.

He was waddling across the room with armfuls of stumps, ready to drop them on me — waddling because he was halfway through tying on a new patented batsman's box, the 'Armalite Trusty', an extraordinary contraption looking like a cotton-duck-and-wadding version of what you might get should you flay an armadillo.

'Quite sure . . . those umpire's coats, too, Tommy.'

I could hear footsteps in the corridor . . . court-shoe heels treading in the inner sanctum of Bellow's club house. Would we lose the fixture? If they caught her we would.

'What d'you think of this?' Tommy said.

He thrust his crotch forward and waggled his hips. I took a chance and presumed he meant his 'Armalite Trusty' rather than the action he'd just demonstrated.

'Super . . .' I hissed, 'quick, more weight, more weight!'

'Do you think it'll work?'

I was covered at last. Tommy pulled the sides of the bag up to make sure. I was panting from the chase but the sheer weight of the covering should hide that.

'If the box doesn't work, Tommy, I guarantee you'll never feel a thing.'

'What was that?' said a distinctly female voice. 'Put some clothes on you. You're disgusting like that . . . where do you think you are?'

'A men's changing room?' ventured Tommy. Fool! He should have just pulled his togs up and hopped it. I would have.

'Don't cheek me, you little whippersnapper. I'm George Lyall's mother-in-law and I want him *now*. Where is he?'

'Not here, Missus. We haven't got him here.'

There followed a few seconds' silence while the Dragon

paced the room, gave everyone's clothes and baggage a good going over.

'Whose are these?' she cried.

'Oh . . . they're mine, actually,' said young Tommy.

'Well, I just hope you don't get knocked down on the way home. What would the hospital think of your poor mother?'

'My Mum doesn't do my washing any more,' said Tommy. 'I'm twenty-three.'

'That's no excuse for *you* not doing it either. Muck is inexcusable, young man . . . why is that bag moving?'

'Bag?' said the brave and faithful Tommy. 'What bag?'

But the game was up.

They took me away still dressed in my whites. We left Patel's car for him and travelled in my Ford. I suppose the Patelettes' grasp of their (other) mother tongue will suffer accordingly; perhaps they'll go through life believing their own language has no definite article, or accusative case or whatever. I've often wondered how it would be if language teaching were organised on solely linear principles . . . 'I'm sorry boy, we covered the German neuter last week. This week we're on subjunctives.' And so a man would be condemned to go through life with no neuter. Perhaps he could be issued with an air horn so that his sentences wouldn't have gaps in them. '*Bitte schön, gnädige Frau, was ist . . .*HONK!'

Things have picked up since my youth. Now people wear headphones and read French and Italian sporting news-papers in class. They're taught 'conversation' by a rather charming young lady from Lyons, whom we have on loan. The Senior Lecturer Foreign Languages is a young man of about twenty-eight who speaks heaven knows how many tongues fluently and is sympathetic and kind to his students. The chap who taught us, on the other hand, wore an academic gown with a specially sewn pocket for his cane . . . and he was about eighty-eight, not twenty-eight.

I remember my first French lesson well. Most of my classmates had been in prep schools or at least sophisticated primary schools. I had not. Green — for such was the old language teacher's name — unfurled a large drawing of a French house and pinned it to the blackboard. We had our visual aids, too.

Green drew his cane like a rapier, slapped the plan with it

and said something which came to my ears as, 'Issy oon gron dimmerbler.'

To my utter amazement my new classmates said, without prompting, 'Issy oon gron dimmerbler.'

Green whacked the plan again and said, 'Say Mess-ewer Tea-Beau, ay sa fam Madam Tea-Beau.'

All the boys said, 'Say Mess-ewer Tea-Beau, ay sa fam Madam Tea-Beau.' I just moved my lips.

'Too, garson!' Green called, slapping the plan of Mayson Tea-Beau with his cane. 'Kes-ker say?'

I thought he'd lost his conkers, completely cracked up. My surprise was complete when a boy in the front row replied, 'Oon gron dimmerbler.'

'Bee-yen. Ay too, key-es?'

He pointed the cane at me. I nearly fainted.

'Ah . . . ah.'

'Deet mwa, key-es.' He looked pretty angry, and he got pretty angry when I said in the forbidden English, 'I'm sorry, sir. I don't know what this is all about.'

He caned me . . . ah yes, we've moved on since those days. When I think back, I'm surprised that any language apart from the native variety survived the likes of Green and his visual aids. Nowdays all our students leave our hands with at least a smattering of both French *and* BBC Basic. So much for the teaching of languages. My task for now was to find the dread Eric, whose mentality centred on the distinctly *non*-verbal. To Swindon.

*

8 p.m. found me searching the highways and byways of Swindon for Eric. He's the reason for this afternoon's panic, he's the reason for my missing out on smoked salmon mousse, champagne and crusting port. The swine. It seems Carol had phoned Elizabeth not long after Patel and I left for the Bellow's match. Eric had disappeared. Carol thought he'd dragged his shattered body somewhere to die. Elizabeth promptly panicked, phoned the Dragon, borrowed the Patels' car and came to fetch me.

Eric has had a nurse over the last few months. He says he's desperately ill, can hardly stagger to the shops, Carol's not around all the time (her 'career' has taken off again . . . she's got herself three lines in a film). Eric's reason may or may not be true . . . I don't know. What I *do* know is that he's hand-picked his nurses for their well-turned ankles and pneumatic bosoms. There have been none of the middle-aged battle-axes I associate with nursing, all broad backs and starched dresses. Big hips and acid tongues. The sort of nurses I've known wouldn't have put up with Green's babbling in foreign codes, nor my playing cricket, nor Eric's over-active imagination. They know where God lives and what the truth is and what the Queen's name is and they also know that these two spoonfuls of pink stuff will get you well again, all you have to do is act grown up and take your medicine . . . be a big boy now, open wide.

I found Eric in his nurse's arms, in The Blacksmith's Arms. They were both a little the worse for wear and could give no account of themselves over the past few hours — the pub had only been open since seven. Since the nurse was a sloe-eyed redhead who looked about eighteen, and since her starchy white frock was looking somewhat crumpled, it didn't need much by way of imagination to guess that what they called their 'country stroll' had ended in, or behind, a hayrick, hedge, barn or whatever shelter man or the seasons had thought to provide.

The nurse excused herself to the loo and never returned. If there's no second door she may — as far as I'm aware — be there even now, trying to sober up and put her bonnet on straight. After ten minutes of waiting for her, I dragged Eric out to the car and dumped him on the back seat. He was merry enough in his own way and had done the things I suppose his life for the most part had consisted of — drinking too much and misbehaving with women younger than himself. In view of what happened next, I suppose it's just as well he'd celebrated his life style in this fashion . . . for, not content with ruining the Bellow's match for me *again*, not content with giving his daughter, my wife, a nervous condition, not content with giving his wife enough pent-up anger and undiluted bile to last her another full year, Eric had the cheek to expire in the back of my Cortina! This, I thought, was nothing less than selfishness. *I* was the one who had to pull up outside his flat and explain, in response to the

139

women's enquiry — 'Have you found him?' — 'Well, yes and no.'

'What do you mean, "yes and no"? Do you have him with you?'

'Uh . . . in a manner of speaking, yes.'

'Then where is he?' cried the Dragon.

I indicated Eric, slumped on the back seat . . . dead as a doornail.

'There.'

What followed was a night to remember, and even as it began I wished I'd found somewhere better to hide than the club bag back at Bellow's. I could, for instance, have stripped off, jumped in the shower and worn a monkey mask . . . that would've put her off the trail. Or I could have simply joined the fielding side . . . they'd never have looked for me there. Or I could have hidden under the dining-room table, or in the loft. I could have borrowed the barman's coat and served drinks. Anything, really anything.

Anything would have been better than this.

Tuesday 6th July
I am just recovering some sort of composure. I had to take both yesterday and today off work . . . just when I didn't want to. Sunday night was an all-night session. It started with recriminations about the demise of Eric. Notwithstanding the fact that he'd been administering booze, women and tobacco to himself for fifty-odd years, an immediate consensus arose among the women gathered outside his flat on Sunday night that he hadn't died; no, I'd killed him. Dying is passive, killing active.

'Take him to the hospital!' Carol called.

'He's dead,' I said.

'Kiss of life!' from my wife.

'He's dead,' I said.

'Somebody call an ambulance . . . please please.' The Dragon lay on the pavement and moaned.

'Dee, ee, ay, dee. He's snuffed it,' I said.

'How can you be so coarse?' said the Dragon. 'Take him to the Hospital.'

'*No*,' I said. 'He's dead. Hospitals are for people who are as yet *not* dead.'

'Why didn't you take him there when you first realised he was ill?' said Elizabeth.

'Because I didn't realise he was ill until he had already expired. I didn't realise until we were at the end of this road.'

I had in fact spent the journey home cracking rather weak jokes at a corpse, I knew, but I decided this wasn't the time to tell her. His first, rather cracked, laugh had apparently been a death rattle. I thought such things only happened in westerns; or in picture books perhaps a death rattle might slip from the lips of a man who'd just said, 'Now you die, Englischer dog!' only to be taken by surprise himself. I never thought they happened in *Swindon*.

We left Eric, or the former Eric, in the back seat of my car and called the police. They took it very seriously and sent a uniformed constable and a 'tec', as we used to call them — Detective Sergeant Broom. The uniformed constable arrived first.

'Where is he?' he asked.

I showed him.

'Where did it happen?'

'As you can see,' I said, 'it happened in the back of my car.'

He took his helmet off and scratched his head.

'The back of a car, sir, is not a place. *Whereabouts* did it happen?'

'Between The Blacksmith's Arms and here.'

'That's not a place, either. Can't you be more specific?'

'No. He was alive when we left there and dead when we arrived here.'

'I don't think you're being as helpful as you possibly could, sir. Didn't he call out, cry for help?'

'No.'

'Didn't he make any noise at all?'

'"Aaaargh" . . . he said "aaaargh".'

'Didn't you find that strange, sir?'

I drew the constable off to one side . . . I didn't want the women to hear.

'I'd just told him a joke,' I said.

'Was it a very bad joke?' he asked.

141

'Quite. It was one of F. S. Trueman's. About a fanatical member of Yorkshire County Cricket Club, and this chap has himself cremated when he dies and the ashes spread at Headingley and . . .'

Well, it made the policeman laugh, anyway. It's nice to meet an official with a sense of humour.

'What's that man laughing at?' said the Dragon.

'He's not . . . he's got a cough, madam,' said the detective, who'd just arrived. 'Righto, constable, take these people upstairs, will you?'

Detective Sergeant Broom was the sort of detective who watches too much t.v. He thinks informality is friendliness, and therefore put himself on first name terms with everyone (him to *us*, I mean. We were expected to go on calling him 'Sergeant'). He told Carol to make some tea, asked me to tell my story.

I did. Then he asked each of the women to tell their stories, which naturally overlapped with mine. Then he sent the women out and said, 'Bumped him off, did you, George?'

'What?'

'Hate him, did you? What was it for, money or just sheer hatred?'

'Do you mind?' I said, 'I'm an HOD.'

'Mind what you say, Lyall. We'll check everything carefully.'

Blue suit, brown shirt, floral pattern tie, Corfam shoes . . . I know all about the likes of Broom. If I hadn't I would have had plenty of time in which to learn on that night, because he kept me there for hours, always questioning, always disbelieving the answers.

'Why would a man in white clothes call to take his father-in-law for a drive, Georgey?'

'I'd just been playing cricket?'

'Oh yes, and . . . no, don't tell me, you were in such a rush to come for him you didn't have time to change?'

'That's right.'

He waved his arms, leaned across Eric and Carol's living-room table and said, 'Just tell me why you did it, Georgey.'

'*My name is not "Georgey"!*' I shouted.

'Oh yes . . . got a bit of a temper, have we?'

At about 3 a.m. we managed to contact Eric's doctor, who

was sea-fishing in Wales. He was able to confirm that Eric had indeed been living on borrowed time since the mid-sixties. Broom was forced to release me . . . though he still muttered darkly about 'checking on everything'. I'm a bit concerned because I did forget to pay for my petrol at a motorway service station some years ago near Metz . . . I wonder if you can be prosecuted in England for pinching petrol in France? It's the sort of question whose answer I should, in theory, know — if Broom finds out about it he'll find a way to prosecute, *I* know . . . a thoroughly nasty piece of work, that young man is.

Thursday 7th July
It has been arranged that we will bury Eric on Saturday. It seems spoiling the Bellow's match wasn't enough for him, even in death! I did mention the Merryton home match on Sunday to Elizabeth, but she kicked up a fuss — made quite a scene of it in the end. Perhaps I should offer to play in black.

I haven't heard from Detective Sergeant Broom, though I've been on tenterhooks. I wonder how long I'd have to wait before I can be sure I have no Interpol file? I don't think I've ever been so glad to see the white cliffs of Dover as I was at the end of that trip to the continent. I spent the entire journey studiously avoiding the eyes of French policemen and officials. Eventually I was stopped and the car searched by customs at Calais. My heart was in my mouth!

The French customs officer (*douanier* — dooannee-ay in Greenspeak) must have been what passes for a humorist on the other side of the *Manche* because he said to me, 'Have you anything to declare, sir?'

'Have Australia got the runs?' I said.

'Australia? . . . no, I meant are you taking anything from France to England?'

Taking anything from France to England! That's a good one.

'No, chum,' I said, 'there's nothing French that we need in England, leaving aside the occasional drop of plonk.'

France isn't even an Associate Member of the ICC! As far

as serious matters go *Fiji* is more important than France . . .
it's just not as convenient to get to.

*

I wonder if things will be back to normal in time for the First
Test against New Zealand — next week. I wonder if things
will be back to normal in time for E. to go to Minorca (i.e. in
time for George to go on tour).

I do hope so.

Friday 8th July
Train to Swindon this afternoon. I had to pick up the faithful
old Cortina. After Sergeant Broom and his colleagues had
spent half the night doing their *Naked City* impersonations,
they went down to remove the cadaver from the car, only to
discover that *rigor mortis* had set in and that no matter how
they puffed, panted and pulled, the body would not come
out of the car. Even in death Eric is obdurate. They had to
hang on to the car till his limbs unstiffened, and today has
been my first chance to collect it. At home again I had to
park two streets away from The Glebe and not mention the
matter of the car at all. Elizabeth will not see, let alone drive
it. On Monday I will go and change it for something else.

I can just imagine the salesman's face.

'Why do you want to sell it sir?'

'Someone died in the back.'

'Oh I think I can solve that problem for you sir . . . there
are some nice little two seaters over here. . . .'

I *dream* of an Audi Quattro. I will *buy* an Austin Metro.
Imagine if Eric had pegged out in the back seat of a two-door
car! They'd never have got him out, *rigor mortis* gone-away
or not-gone-away. I will bear this in mind in choosing our
new car. I'll make the Dragon ride always in the front, unless
I can find a suitable estate model, in which case I will have a
ready-made coffin installed in the back for elderly passengers
to ride in.

144

Saturday 9th July
Buried Eric. A very quiet and controlled wake.

Sunday 10th July
Not many laughs to be had today. No radio, no telly. Dark looks from E. every time I peek out of the window . . . well, it's *sunny!* A chap can't be expected to be miserable for his whole life. It's not fair. I can't even have the radio on for the John Player League.

Wednesday 13th July
I feel as if we're on the home straight . . . the summer hols approach. Only fourteen more days! Wonderful. Only sixteen days until we tour! Even better. Elizabeth is staying in Corsham and rang last night to say she thinks she shouldn't go on holiday. I offered to pay for her mother to go too.

'Then I definitely wouldn't go. It's supposed to be a *holiday.*'

In desperation I went over to the Merediths and asked Christina to ring her.

I hope it works.

3 p.m. Coco called me down to his office.

'Here, George, is a copy of the ad we're putting in the *Times Ed. Supp.*'

I'm the sort of man who can take a hint, though it's odd to apply for a job you already hold. To be scrupulously fair I called in Leonard Footle, our twenty-eight-year-old S.L. Languages and Maureen Tate, S.L. Social Studies (and a regular Xanthippe) and put the position to them, that the ad. was going in, that a notice would go on the board as a matter of course, but they might miss it in the end-of-term rush, that they were the best qualified people to do the job (apart

145

from myself and any outside applicants, though I didn't say this). It was a bit devious of me, really, because he's too young and she's too shrewish for Coco's taste.

'Of course *any* member of staff is entitled to apply,' I said.

'Of course.'

'Interviews to be held at the beginning of next term. All that. Of course, I'm not guaranteeing anything, just telling you when they are.'

'Course, George,' said Leonard, 'I don't think *I* for one will bother applying, if *you* are. You're an obvious choice.'

'No no,' said Maureen, 'nor me. It's a lot of writing out and all for a job that you're such an obvious candidate for, George.'

'How kind,' I said. 'I wonder if one of you would like to get a little collection up for the retiring HOD. He's discharged and at home now.'

They agreed.

Later I went out to the workroom. Both Leonard Footle and Maureen Tate were busily scribbling at their desks, and they both put their hands over their papers when I came out, as if they'd been caught copying each other's prep. So much for 'I won't bother'! Perhaps they would get on better with Coco than I'd imagined.

Saturday 16th July

A scorcher. Our return match against Mugsborough Police. Obviously their County HQ had heard of their recent drubbing at our hands, because they had loaned a cadet who was six feet four tall, about the same across the shoulders and appeared to be still growing. All the rest of his team had to do was not get out. I'm not saying this chap was strong on the leg side . . . I'll simply draw a scoring chart *à la* Bill Frindall. . . .

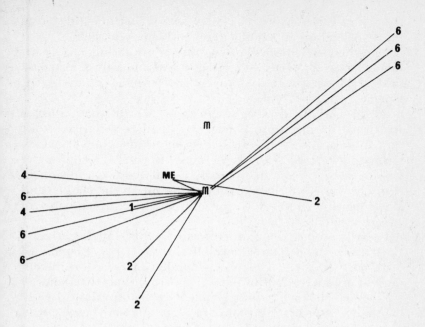

I've only drawn one end . . . but the other, I'm afraid, was the same. If you put a ball on the off side he simply hit it for six. At least on his legs we managed to keep some of them down to twos! The single is where I was fielding at backward square leg. I moved to a sort of short mid-wicket and blow me if Tommy Tonker (as we dubbed the cadet) didn't take two off my shins. Those are the two marked at cover point. By that stage we had Patel doing his Abdul Qadir impersonation to a field set to what I can only characterise as the Mugsborough leg-trap theory . . . that is, with only the bowler, the wicketkeeper and mid-off *not* on the leg side. George Jolly's method in setting this field was to place mid-off, then to take the rest of us down to the leg boundary and call, 'Okay boys, spread out.'

Mike Brearley eat your heart out!

Though set a gigantic 211 to chase, George Jolly was all for going for it . . . I don't know if he knew something about our batsmen I didn't. Tommy Butcher and I managed to play negatively for the better part of ninety minutes, thereby forcing a draw. At one time a police inspector (you can tell, the others called him 'sir') came down the wicket and said to me, 'Not making much of a game of it, are you, bat?'

I pointed to Tommy Tonker, who was walking back to his mark, all sweaty clothes, bulging thighs and flared nostrils. I said, 'I haven't noticed him around town in a panda car, Charlie.'

'Huh,' said the inspector, who knew he didn't have a leg to stand on. Trying it on, as ever . . . just like when they take you to court for dangerous driving when you've merely bumped a bollard. Just like Sergeant Broom in Swindon . . . chancers, every one of them. If I'd signed a confession in Swindon no doubt they'd have slung me in the chokee and I'd be rotting there even now. This is how miscarriages of justice occur.

I scored seventeen not out! All by playing negatively. Perhaps I should make myself the Geoffrey Boycott of Mugsborough . . . or Tavaré, the Zen Batsman. Unfortunately most of my successful innings was due to the fact that Tommy Tonker bowled very quickly but very inaccurately. I only had to defend my stumps once or twice an over. I can hardly count on every bowler I meet being so generous. Tommy Butcher, our wicketkeeper, was thirty-two not out at the other end.

Sunday 17th July
Our club single-wicket mid-season festival.

We draw lots for who plays whom. I drew Jenkins in the first round. Over the past few years I've drawn either Rudi Brathweight, Jenkins or Brian Cook . . . all of them decent all-rounders. What it means is that I get hit all over the ground off my bowling, then can barely defend my wicket against their bowling. It's most unfair, I think. There should be a bit of seeding to give us all an even chance.

Jenkins, as ever, bowled a series of quick, rising balls on the leg side. I may well go and buy a plastic goldfish bowl of the type worn by test cricketers if he keeps this up! I scored thirteen during my three overs but my wicket fell once . . . leaving me with three. I also had contusions to the left lug-hole, a bruise on my cheek and it hurts in my ribs when I laugh. I gave up counting after the first twenty he took off my bowling.

The upshot of all that is that mugs like me (and Patel and young Tommy Butcher) have to stand around in the field all day while more skilful players feed their fantasies . . . be it I.T. Botham for Jenkins, I.V.A. Richards for Brathweight, D.I. Gower for Peterson, whoever. We have to stand around with sticky hands and swollen feet, with red foreheads and parched tongues while other men act out their *Boy's Own* adventures. If yesterday's performance is anything to go by, the best I can aspire to now is a batting performance of the T.G. Evans variety . . . no joy there for the single-wicket competitor.

*

7.45 p.m. Finished at last. Time to roast ox, sip cider (all right, gulp) butter pitta bread and feel guilty about the wife I've left behind me . . . with her mother. In fact the final of our competition was a classic. For the first time in many years George Jolly took the matter seriously, and reached the final. He was matched against Peterson — Jenkins and Brathweight having been seen off in the semis. Now, Peterson bats beautifully but doesn't bowl too well, Jolly bowls pea-shooters and hardly ever bats — he describes himself as a 'specialist slip fielder and bar prop'. Against George's extraordinary bowling Peterson could only manage sixteen . . . but the shock of the evening was the sight of George running quick singles off *Peterson's* bowling. Late fifties, fat, grey-haired, out of practice (for batting *and* bowling), red-cheeked and with his grandchildren calling him on from the boundary, George won. The hare and the tortoise! I loved it, even though I could barely stand at the end.

Jennifer Cook turned up during our barbecue (if we didn't exactly roast an ox we had enough fires to!). She came up to my side once and pulled my arm, but then turned shy and dashed off when some others came over. Later she came back and said, 'George, I *must* speak to you.'

What a fine jawline she has. I mustn't let my mind wander so, but what perfect white teeth. Could she somehow have felt the pure animal power in my presence? Could there be

149

more to ESP, mind-contact, astrology, all that, than a sceptic like myself will ordinarily admit? I *was* wearing my new stretch-fit whites and a rather expensive grey guernsey, so I suppose I did cut quite a dash. I let her wait — there's no sense in rushing — allowed her to see what I flatter myself is an aristocratic profile, turned round and drawled, 'Let's talk.'

But she'd gone. Scene-stealer Patel had approached without my seeing him.

'Goodnight, Jenny,' he called to her as she disappeared into the gloom. 'Have you a crick in your neck, George?'

'*No!*' A crick indeed!

'All right, keep a civil tongue in your head. I've brought you a hamburger.'

Perhaps I received the just deserts of a man with impure thoughts. I drowned my sorrows in scrumpy and walked somewhat unsteadily home to my sun-lounger in the study.

Monday 18th July
At supper tonight the Dragon, ever present these days, said, 'A *woman* called for George today.'

'Oh, who?' said my wife. The invisible man sat on his invisible chair munching invisible tortelloni off an invisible plate.

'She wouldn't say.'

'Wouldn't say?' repeated Elizabeth.

I reached an invisible hand out and grabbed the tomato sauce (real, bright red, Italian stuff, of course).

'No,' said the Dragon, 'she said she was the captain's wife.'

'Captain's wife, eh? I wonder what Elspeth Jolly wants with George. Was she a really fat woman in her late fifties, very maternal looking?'

'I don't know dear, she was on the phone.'

'Of course . . . what could she want with George?'

I took advantage of this new-found invisibility to slip out to The Dog and Bucket for a quick one. When I came back the Dragon said, 'I hope you're not going to be doing that every night . . . we all know where that leads' (this last pointing at the door), and began to cry.

150

Elizabeth brought in another bulk-supply box of Kleenex from the lavatory (why is the lavatory associated with blowing your nose?) and peeled off a hundred or so hankies for the Dragon.

'Jennifer Cook phoned for you, George. It was she who rang earlier, not Elspeth.'

'What did she say?' The invisible man's voice boomed from an empty sofa.

'Oh, she has to speak to you. She says it definitely has to be you.'

If anyone could have seen me, they might have seen me flush. As it was I just stayed invisibly there all night, reading an invisible book by the non-existent John Arlott about a match which presumably never took place.

Friday 22nd July
Lunchtime I slipped out to the sports shop and purchased a pair of Sockopads, shinpads on a hose as worn by judo persons. I have a very nasty bruise on my shin from Tommy Tonker's on-drive (or whatever you'd call such an unconventional but massively struck shot).

Saturday 23rd July
Mugsborough Seconds, at home.

Mugsborough Firsts are a league side, and although their Seconds are something of a scratch outfit, they're not without the competitive league 'edge' of the Firsts. Most of the Seconds play at one time or other in the year for the Firsts. They tend to be an aggressive side, not past a bit of gamesmanship; bowling beamers and 'talking-up' or 'sledging' the batsman not being the half of it. Because they're local, it's a needle match and we try to turn out our strongest side.

Much hilarity was occasioned in the dressing room when I produced the Sockopads, though I think some of my fellow players had the opportunity to rue their laughter when a teenage batsman came in at number three and proceeded to on- and off-drive hard and fast along the ground on our sometime rugby pitch. One or two of the players would have been pleased to have Sockopads on their chests and faces, methinks.

We were left 155 to chase, went for it and were all out at 121 . . . a crushing defeat given the nature of the match. I scored two before I was caught fending off a rather nasty ball before my face . . . even the Sockopads wouldn't help that one.

Perhaps I should think about one of those plastic goldfish bowls for my face.

Sunday 24th July
GCHQ Minders, at home.

A game we failed to finish, though this time it was not the fault of the weather. After a remarkable innings on our part, remarkable both for the low score — 77 — and for the fact that Tommy Butcher drove one ball and failed to hold on to his bat properly; the bat went to mid-off, the ball to mid-on, mid-off caught the bat but mid-on dropped the ball — the Minders were left with an easy target. No sooner had their captain opened the batting, though, than Mrs Knightly ran on the field with a typewritten message for him — delivered, she said, by motorcycle messenger. The Minders' captain is a man of little charm and, it seems, less reading ability, for he stood at the crease with the paper saying, 'Tee, haich, ee . . . *the*. Arr, you, ess, ess. . . .'

Until Patel snatched the document from his hand and read, 'The Russians are coming. Return immediately.'

Without another word they left the field, changed and piled into their cars.

'You know you're forfeiting the match!' I cried into the dust-storm, but they didn't answer.

*

10 p.m. Called the Minders' Hon. Sec. to protest at the curtailment of today's match.

'What happened?' I said.

'Oh . . . it's okay. It was a false alarm at work. Practice run. Terribly sorry. We'll make it up to you next season.'

Our committee will have to decide, though, whether there should be a 'next season' with such an unreliable lot. I would be against it. With so few weeks available in which to play the summer sport it seems reckless to be involved with such a crowd. 'The Russians are coming. Return immediately' is probably code for 'Free beer at the GCHQ Minders' Social Club this evening, chaps, so don't mess around there!'

'We're not a mere rugby club, you know,' I said to their Hon. Sec. 'We're a serious cricket side with a long tradition. When we start a match we like to finish it.'

'You'll have to take up rugby fixtures with the rugby club secretary, Mr Lyall,' he said.

Sometimes I feel that *all* phones are fitted with scramblers.

Wednesday 27th July
End of term . . . hooray! The only black cloud on the horizon is the advent of exam results in August. I'll try to forget that for now.

Down to The Pig and Paunch, the Mugsborough College humanities staff watering-hole, for the traditional end-of-term-end-of-year-how-on-earth-did-we-ever-get-through-that-? booze-up. A round of drinks is usually provided courtesy of the HOD . . . i.e. yours truly. Forty-odd people went — I'll have to re-mortgage the house!

Nothing had been said about the permanent job, though Spite turned up to collect the teaching profession's version of a retirement gong. . . . a cut-glass vase, a book token, a year's subscription to *Private Eye*, a glass of champagne plus a tearful farewell from people who a mere six months before were saying behind your back that they hated your guts and would cheerfully kill you if they had the chance. Now they shake your hand and kiss your cheek and manage to stammer out between sobs that they're personally de-va-stat-ed by the loss of your services. It will happen to me in some years' time, I know. Today it's happening to Spite. There's only one way for the victim to get his own back . . . the traditional speech. Spite's was an exceptional example of the form,

153

taking over forty minutes and meandering from anvil and apocalypse to zephyr and zinc via history, the training of teachers, the need for reform of the Mental Health Act, a novel order of atomic weights Spite had cooked up on his own and a spirited if inaccurate version of his own life in which he cast himself as a misunderstood Mr Chips. Since we had hired the back room of The Pig and Paunch specially for the occasion, and since that room has no bar, the throng had to shift from foot to foot and simply *wait* until he'd finished. I'm sure he did it on purpose.

After Spite had done everyone organised themselves into rounds for their drinks . . . everyone except me, of course. *I* was left out.

'Got no drink?' someone called, coming back with a trayful.

'I'd buy you a drink, George, but we're in a whip here,' said young Carl Norton.

Charming! I sloped off early, telling myself it's not really my scene, that I had things to do. Eventually I found myself outside the town sports shop.

'Got any cricketing helmets?' I asked the boy inside.

I didn't know I was addressing a philosopher.

'I've got safety glasses for carpet bowls, protective gloves for tennis ball boys, bum pads for jockeys made out of featherlight airmail packaging, I've got leather strops for razor-sharp squash players . . . but I ain't got no cricketing helmets.'

'None at all?'

'I've got boxes, jocks and shin pads.'

'Could you order me one?'

'Bowling shirts, Aussie hats, pimple caps and batting gloves.'

'Show me a catalogue?'

'Score-books, balls, bails, bats, Indian flannel trousers.'

'Or let me know when your rep is calling?'

'Elbow pads, chest pads, thigh pads, batsmen's inner gloves, keeper's gloves of various types.'

'Oh well never mind.' I made for the door. He followed me.

'I've got cricket boots, shoes and trainers. I've got pimple sole or leather sole, spikes and no spikes. I've got *Know the*

Game handbooks, charts of cricket techniques, photographs of old cricket players . . . *but I ain't got no cricketing helmets!*'

He was red in the face, angry.

'Why does it bother you so?' I said.

'Because every year you people come up with some new and exotic item which you expect me to have here . . . and I can't cope! This is a little town and a little shop! I'm keeping my little wife short of the little money I have so I can stock this place.'

He sat down on the ground and began to cry. A wife! I'd thought of him as barely being out of short trousers.

'Did you go to Mugsborough College?' I asked.

'Yes . . . I did business studies.' And he stood, closed the door and bolted it behind me. I felt like raking Charlie Baker out of the Business Studies booze-up and showing him what wretched lives his rugged individualistic creed has led to.

I walked back through town. I felt miserable, left out. A car beeped its horn and I turned angrily.

'I'll take as long as I want on a zebra . . . oh . . . hello.'

It was Coco in his flashy Alfa Romeo.

'Lift, George?'

'I'm okay thanks. You don't go my way,' I said. Though it was true I'd take him out of his way, the main thing was I didn't want to talk to him. I didn't want to talk to anyone.

'Come on. Get in.' He opened the passenger door.

I should have guessed we hadn't met by accident.

'I saw you slide out of your departmental booze-up. Too sober-minded to drink during the day, eh George?'

'Something like that, Mr Channel.'

'Good. Thought I'd let you know, interviews are next week. Monday. You'll get a letter in due course.'

'Interviews?' I was still somewhere between the pub and the sports shop.

Coco snapped through the gearchange like an ageing Jim Clark. We accelerated fiercely. Old ladies dashed for the kerb, children hid behind parked cars, a policeman ducked into a shop doorway. I felt as if I were in that Brighton express train film they used to show during 'short interludes' on telly.

'Yes. For your job. I mean, we have to go through the

system, you know. The county wouldn't put up with us simply plonking you into the job. We have to draw up shortlists, get references, hold interviews. All that.'

We forced a cyclist into a ditch.

'Does that mean I'll have to come for an interview during the hols?' I asked.

'Well, George — GET OUT OF THE ROAD YOU B****Y FOOL! — either you want the job or you don't. I shouldn't think one day during the vacs would do you any harm.'

'No I didn't mean that. I meant . . . oh, I dunno.'

We screeched to a halt at the corner of The Glebe. Mothers ran onto lawns and dragged their children to safety. There wasn't another car in sight, just a faint blue haze on the road behind us.

'You mean you thought it was in the bag, didn't you, George?'

'Well. . . .'

'Don't worry. You've got the form, you're already in the job . . . don't worry. Wear a sober suit on Monday and don't be late . . . apart from that. . . .'

'Well?'

'Well.'

'Oh . . . *well.*'

He let me get most of the way out of the car before he drove off. I stood at the roadside surrounded by burnt rubber and oil fumes.

Well.

Thursday 28th July

6 a.m. Up early so I can get a full day's worrying in. By Monday I'll be a stretcher case. There was a letter waiting for me at home when Coco let me off (as I think of getting out of his car) yesterday.

'*Dear Mr Lyall, With reference to your application for the post of Head of Department, would you attend for interview at the college on Monday August 1 . . . .*' etc.

It sent me into a blue funk. I never knew the job meant so much to me.

This morning there was another letter waiting, delivered by hand and marked, '*To G.V. Lyall Esq. Absolutely Personal*'.

It was from Jennifer Cook! and it read, '*Dear George, I absolutely must speak to you in private soon. I know that this is a busy time for you, what with you being made HOD at the College, but I wonder if I could impose on you for just a few minutes? We've got so much to talk about and I fear we must do it soon or I will be ashamed before you and Elizabeth for ever.*

(Signed) *Jennifer* (and an 'X' too!)

I could barely contain myself. What mystery! What flattery! Of course our home phone wouldn't be secure, so I slipped a jacket on and ran down to the phone box.

'Jenny, my sweet.'

'Who's this?'

'*George.*'

'George?'

'George Lyall.'

'Oh hullo George. Gosh, it's terribly early to phone.'

She sounded drowsy.

'I should have waited but I couldn't. Once I had your note I just had to speak.'

'Oh yes. I'm sorry about that. I just didn't want it to go past this weekend. When can we see each other?'

'Whenever you want!' I said . . . oh, the excitement of behaving terribly, terribly badly . . . like breathing pure oxygen. 'What are you wearing?'

'Wearing? I'm in bed, George. What a question!'

In bed!

'Tell me, please,' I said.

'Oh, all right, I'm in the buff . . . doesn't everyone sleep in the buff nowdays? What is this, a survey?'

Wit, humour, a rich voice, a beautiful neck *and* she sleeps in the buff. I can't bear it. Elizabeth has me organised all day tomorrow, so I have fixed to see Jennifer after Saturday's home match. I reeled from the phone box feeling like a teenager, hands all atremble, dry-mouthed. I'd hardly even noticed that the phone box (like all phone boxes, it seems) doubles as a public urinal.

'Where have you been?' barked Sergeant-Major Mrs Lyall when I returned.

'After the paperboy!' I called up the stairs. 'He'd delivered the wrong paper.' I'd take her tea in bed, I thought. Alleviate my conscience.

She was in the kitchen, *Guardian* open on her lap. She lifted it for me to see.

'Did I say paperboy? I meant postman. He'd delivered next door's mail.'

'And?'

'Oh . . . there was nothing for us.'

A soft plop came from the hallway.

'Do you think he's traded his bike for a boomerang?'

'Probably just a bit confused. It *is* early, after all, Elizabeth. Perhaps he's a new postman.'

I shouldn't even try to lie. I'm so awful at it.

'Don't forget we're taking Mummy home tomorrow,' she said.

How could I?

Saturday 30th July

A West Indian touring team. The strangely named 'Reunion XI' consists for the main part of Western Region British Rail employees. It seems that they don't get enough of our part of the world on their (in some cases daily) excursions from Paddington. The Reunion XI tours Somerset. I'm not sure how we came by the fixture; people mention Rudi Brathweight's half-brother but I'm certain he's a glazier . . . there can't be many of those on BR. I've never seen him with the Reunion crowd, anyway.

However we came by them, Reunion XI are loved, welcomed . . . indeed fêted by us Hacks for one reason — one reason apart, that is, from the usual reasons one might love, welcome and fête a group of men.

They give Jenkins his come-uppance. Year after year after year.

It's an 11 a.m. start. People do like to get their money's worth when they're touring. Who can blame them? Not I.

Jenkins is always at the ground before anyone else on the day of the Reunion match. I should think if you went there at 5 a.m. he'd be prowling outside the gate, 'coffin' bag in one hand, Duncan Fearnley bat in the other.

By the time we've arrived and the visitors have arrived,

Jenkins has walked the outfield, knows every blade of the track and has measured a run for himself at both ends.

By the time we've changed Jenkins is in a foul mood, only having had the boundary boards and our little wooden pavilion-cum-changing-room to get angry at all morning.

By the time we're on the field he's wound himself up into a condition where he won't even look at the opposition and contents himself with venting his anger on one of our players — usually me.

He was true to form.

'Hullo, Phil old chap. How are things?' I said.

'Things will be all right as long as you don't (foul word) around all through the (foul word)ing game, dropping catches and making stupid (foul word)ing jokes, you (foul word).'

Choice!

He wandered round for a few more minutes, getting angry at anything that crossed his path, then was surprised to be sent by George Jolly, our wily old captain, down to the mid-off boundary. Jolly started the game with Brathweight at one end for speed and Patel at the other for variety. This confused the Reunion people, who'd been used to starting the match against Jenkins and Brathweight. The tactic worked. After twenty overs our visitors were fifty-five for four.

And Jenkins was champing at the bit.

George Jolly brought him on. This was Jenkins' chance. He extended his run to about fifty paces, charged down to the crease and bowled a scorchingly fast ball. The batsman drove it back over Jenkins' head for four.

Jenkins did it again.

So did the batsman.

When Jenkins walked back to bowl his third ball, his fingers were white on the ball, his eyes were popping, he stared straight in front of himself.

He ran down and bowled a beamer, as fast as he could. The batsman, a squat Antiguan with enormous biceps, hooked another four. Tommy Butcher leapt up from behind the stumps and clapped, then, catching Jenkins' eye, added belatedly and guiltily, 'Oh . . . *well bowled*, Phillip. Well bowled.' Which it patently was not.

By his third over Jenkins was reduced to serving up long

hops . . . just as his hero Botham has been doing at Leeds to our New Zealand visitors. In fairness to Botham, everyone else has bowled shockingly. Jenkins deserves no such allowance.

Reunion scored 190 in all, and we played out for a draw. I believe these longer games always end in a draw. I dread to think what would happen if players of our standard played test matches over four or five days. There would be ten innings each and the matter would still be unresolved at the end. The only way of making a match out of *our* sort of cricket is the 'sporting declaration'.

I had a swift drink with the West Indians. Charlie, the Antiguan, asked why we're all so pleased to see Jenkins hammered.

'Because he's a swine. Because you're the only people who seem to be able to do it to him. Because we all hate him,' I said.

As a swap for this confession, Charlie told me his side were called 'Reunion' because they only get together to tour.

'Don't you play the rest of the year?' I asked.

'I don't. Most of the fellows don't. Some do. We just come down here for a cricket tour because it's a nice holiday.'

A nice holiday! Jenkins trying to rip your head off is a holiday to these people. I didn't dare ask how they amused themselves over Christmas. They'd probably want a regular fixture with the Patel clan.

My own batting performance deserves to have a veil drawn over it. Suffice to say I tried to play off my back foot when I was out of practice, when I didn't have my eye in, when the track was misbehaving, when the Reunion bowler had had plenty of time to practice getting the ball on a spot. L.b.w.! A duck! Quack quack quack. I am desolated. Why me?

*

10 p.m. Nipped into the loo to splash on just a drop more Eau Sauvage, then the plan was to slip off before anyone noticed. Some hopes.

'Is that you that smells like an 'arlot's 'andbag, Rudi, or me?'

Rudi Brathweight and Charlie the stunted Antiguan were

160

outside the loo door, sipping lager and planning next year's campaign.

'No!' cried Rudi. He gave Charlie his glass, threw his arms around me and gave me a whacking great kiss on the forehead. 'It's this beautiful young lady here. Hold me back . . . I don't think I can control meself!'

So much for quiet exits. I eventually arrived at Jennifer's house at ten-thirty. It was a beautiful, warm July night and she was on the front lawn.

'George!' she cried in a hoarse whisper and pointed to the pathway at the side of the house.

I went into the darkness. She followed. The wall loomed on one side, a privet hedge on the other.

'Jennifer,' I whispered.

'George.'

'Jennifer.' I put my arms about her waist.

'*George*!' She pulled back.

'*Jennifer*.' I was surprised.

'George,' said another voice.

'Brian!' I exclaimed.

'Don't shout, don't shout,' he said.

'I thought you were in Spain,' I hissed.

'All will be explained.' He took my arm and led me down the path. A hurricane lamp glowed in the little potting shed at the bottom of their garden. We went in.

And everything was explained.

Sunday 31st July

A rest day in the Leeds Test. A rest day for me too . . . I've cried off today. Part of it's because I've a Very Important Day Tomorrow, part of it because I'm on a pair (not for the first time this season) and I don't think I should subject my nerves or my morale to a possible disaster when I've so much on my plate on Monday.

After breakfast E. was to drive over to her mother's house for the day. I insisted first, though, that we went and looked at the patio windows.

'They haven't leaked for ages,' I said.

'It's *summer*, George. Nothing leaks during the summer.'

'I think it's mainly condensation anyway.'

'There shouldn't *be* any condensation.'

'P3W is about to go bankrupt,' I said.

'How do you know?' Elizabeth flopped back on the sofa and started thumbing through the *Sunday Times* mag. 'And if you're sure we should get a lawyer.'

'We've been through all that . . . anyway, there's more to it.'

'What?'

'I went and saw Jennifer Cook last night. Brian owns P3W.'

'*What?*' She dropped the magazine.

'And it's going skint and he hasn't been to Spain at all. He's been hiding from creditors in their potting shed for the last six months and she's terribly upset and ashamed and can't face us unless he comes clean because finding out he's let us down too is the last straw for her. . . .' I knew I was rambling, but the whole wretched story of Brian's failure as a business man rambled out in one form or another.

'And he's given up cricket forever,' I said. 'He says he's too old.'

'But he's the same age as you, George.'

'Thank you.'

My wife has what people call 'a way with words'.

'Has he really not been to Spain?' she said.

'White as a sheet. That card was sent from Spain by a friend of his.'

She abandoned me to Smash of the Day, World at One and Gardener's Question Time. I could have gone to Corsham and had a proper Sunday lunch. Having a hamburger for lunch, though, is a small price to pay for missing a whole afternoon with the Dragon. No doubt she'd turn maudlin before the pudding, and spend an hour or so telling us what a wonderful man Eric was underneath it all. No doubt Mrs Stalin or Eva Braun could have offered a similar homespun account of their loved ones. I'd even prefer to have lunch with one of them, I think. . . . When I pointed out to E. that we'd only returned the Dragon to her lair yesterday she said: 'So what?'

'Well, don't you think going there for lunch the day after you've taken her back is a bit . . . ?'

'A bit what?' she growled. 'A bit thick' I thought. And then

162

before I spoke I thought of cricket tours and wives in Spain, the quiet life. I thought of missing the lot of them for a few days . . . bliss.

'A bit of a nice thing to do. Would you like to read the *Review* before me? Can I get you some more coffee?' I'm getting like Coco. After coffee we looked over the patio windows and decided there was hardly anything wrong with them . . . well, not enough to harass our good friends the Cooks about, anyway. It's hardly right to let a little drop of water come between old friends.

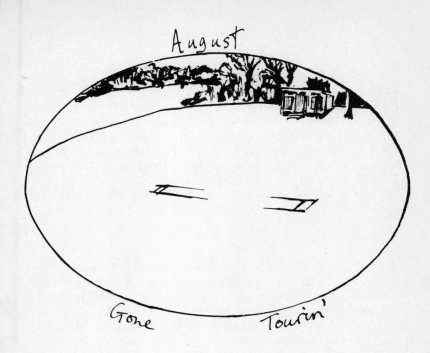

August

Gone   Tourin'

Monday 1st August
At 8.00 the phone rang.
  'Mr Lyall?'
  'Yes.'
  'I wonder what time you'll be down to pick up your new Metro.'
  '*What?*'
  'Your new car, sir. It's been on order for two weeks. Today's the start of the new registrations.'
  'Hang on.'
  I shook E.
  'What do you know about a new car?'
  'Oh that's okay. Tell him I'll be down about ten.' And she rolled over and went back to sleep.
  'My wife will be down about ten for it.'
  'Good.'
  'What colour is it?' I asked.
  'Yellow, sir. Sundance yellow. As ordered.'

Yellow! A new Metro! And a Sundance yellow one at that! So much for consultation.

*

11.30. Staff Coffee Lounge. As I expected, there were several outsiders there for interview. I hadn't really expected Maureen Tate or Leonard Footle to get this far, though.

'Ah, the home team,' Coco said when he came in. 'I'll ask the people who aren't local to see us first, so perhaps you'd like to come back after lunch?'

Leonard and Maureen, I noticed, hardly dared catch my eye.

*

5 p.m. I feel as if I have been dragged through a hedge. My clothes are sweaty and uncomfortable, my feet have swollen inside my new leather shoes, my head aches and I feel sick.

I was the last one to be interviewed. Coco was the only one on the interview panel I know . . . I've *seen* the chairman of the governors before, I've *seen* the county advisor before . . . but I don't *know* them. I'm rather glad I don't, really.

The first problem was my voice. It went up an octave. Then I couldn't find anywhere to put my hands . . . they've always been on the ends of my arms, I don't see why their presence should suddenly become a problem in my thirty-ninth year. Then there were the questions. I'd practised answers to things like, 'What would you do if a female member of staff came to complain about a difficult boy?' or, 'What changes would you like to see in the rota system for exam invigilation?' (I had an extensive answer prepared for that one). I even had one ready for, 'And are there any questions you'd like to ask us, Mr Lyall?' which of course is actually a question about *you* . . . people aren't so much interested in what you're going to ask, they're interested to see whether or not you can think up an intelligent question to ask.

What I *hadn't* prepared was a sort of vox pop version of *New Society*.

'Given current socio-economic trends, Mr Lyall, how *valid* would the preparation of primary source material regarding

166

the cultural set of those of non-British national orientation be with regard for the demands that might be made on such persons in later life . . . would she/he be assisted in any valid way in coming to terms with the situation she/he might be plunged into once formal education had run its course?' asked the advisor, a shrewish-looking woman in her mid-forties wearing no make-up.

I said, 'Sorry?' which clearly wasn't the right answer.

At about the fourth attempt Coco leaned towards me, nodded sagely and said, 'What we want to know, Geo . . . *Mr Lyall*, is "do you think we ought to teach Caribbean or Asian or African history to those students who require it?"'

'Oh, I see,' I said. 'Well, the answer to that one is quite simple.'

They all sat back in their chairs, visibly relieved.

'It's a long question which requires a short answer,' I said.

'Well?' said the advisor, opening and closing her biro.

'Only if it's on the syllabus.' I said.

She dropped her biro. She didn't expect me to get it right on the button like that, *I* know. You don't fool G.V. Lyall with complicated questions. The Gordian Knot wouldn't have foxed me for one minute.

She asked a few more questions, using Coco as interpreter. I answered them okay, though I must say I think sociologists have developed a language all of their own. I was a bit disappointed that no one had asked what outside interests I had, how long I'd been involved with the college, all that. I had the answers to those prepared . . . still, given my initial nervousness, I didn't acquit myself too badly. I was left, however, with an uneasy feeling that Miss Vinegar Face wasn't entirely on my side.

*

8 p.m. Elizabeth agrees that the patio windows hardly leak at all. I agree that yellow isn't a bad colour for an Austin Metro (though in my mind I cross my fingers and think: If and only if you *must* have an Austin Metro). We both agree we need a drink and take the Merediths down to the pub. He is happy, she is happy, E. is happy, G. is happy. I related the interview to them and the sort of ridiculous questions I was

167

asked. They didn't find them as funny as I did . . . well, I've never been any good at telling funny stories. E. and Christina are in a good mood, though. Their sunny Spanish holiday is imminent. Good. So's the tour.

Friday 5th August
5 a.m. Up with the larks to drive the ladies to Cardiff airport. They were supposed·to be going from Heathrow, but with the reliability for which the travel trade is famous Elizabeth received a letter on Wednesday telling her the price had gone up by fifty quid 'owing to currency fluctuation' and the flight had been swapped from Heathrow to Cardiff 'owing to circumstances beyond our control'. It's not so bad for us, but I'm sure anyone travelling from Maidstone or Colchester would be a bit miffed. One day a travel agent will write and say that 'owing to currency fluctuations' the price had gone down by fifty quid. That'll be the same week Papua New Guinea wins its first Test Match in England. A few years ago I might have written, 'That'll be the same week New Zealand wins its first Test Match in England' . . . but of course then I didn't know how Mr R.D.(Z). Willis and his friends would come along and change the scene. On Monday New Zealand scored their first Test victory over us.

*

12.30 p.m. Patel arrives in his cousin's Ford Transit, kindly loaned to us for the tour. The back of the Ford Transit was filled from floor to roof with a large dark object.

'Are we dropping that off somewhere?' I said as I squeezed myself and all my luggage in the front.

'Certainly not,' he said. 'It's our tent.'

I hardly dared turn to take another gander at it.

'You *can't* be serious!'

'George, when have you known me not to be serious? It's our tent.'

'How will we manage Biggsy?'

Patel looked full of confidence, propped up on a cushion so he could see over the steering wheel.

168

'We'll manage,' he said.

Biggs's reaction to the tent was much like mine.

'What's that?'

'It's our tent,' I said, 'and you're going in there with it.'

'You *can't* be serious.'

We were though, for there was no room in the front.

First of all we tried to get him in by the simple expedient of opening the rear doors, shoving Biggs against the tent and then closing them again. Not only could we not get the doors closed on Biggs, but when we dragged his crumpled little body clear we couldn't close them on the tent again.

'Ooh . . . ooh . . . is he all right?' said Mrs Biggs, circling us like a mother hen. 'Should I make you all some more tea?'

We took the tent out and refolded it, which was a bit of a mistake because we had then to beg help from every man in the street to help us lift it back; and it was an even worse fit than before. Patel suggested prising two of the folds apart and inserting Biggs between them. We tried it.

'It's no good,' I said, 'he's not stiff enough.'

'Ooh . . . ooh . . . is he all right?' said Mrs Biggs.

'No!' said Biggs, half in and half out of a tent-fold, the upper part of his body protruding through the van's rear doors. 'He is not all right.'

'Ooh . . . ooh. . . .'

We solved the problem by squeezing him between the tent and the roof. You could hear from the hoarse wheezing that he could breathe all right, though his voice was too muffled to hold a conversation. As we drove out of Mugsborough I could swear I heard him humming the 'Internationale'.

Saturday 6th August

I am waiting to bat in our opening match against Little Lumpton on Sea . . . *sur mer*, as Paul Peterson insists on calling it. He thinks that's a grand joke.

Yesterday was appalling. I don't know how many years we've been touring in Sussex, yet we never find our way to Lumpton at the first attempt. I think the only way we could guarantee it would be if a motorway were to be driven across Wilts and Hants. It should start in Mugsborough town centre and end on Little Lumpton village green. Failing such a feat of civil engineering, Patel and I had to rely on maps and each other's sketchy grasp of the mechanics of map-reading. It didn't work very well.

Seven hours after leaving Mugsborough we found ourselves on Brighton seafront. We had come via Portsmouth, Salisbury, Basingstoke, Woking and the M23 Motorway, in that order. We'd filled the tank of the Transit twice, changed the plugs once and very nearly blew the head-gasket on a hill outside Salisbury. We had also stopped in all the places I've mentioned and many others so that Biggs might use the lavatories. From his hidey-hole in the roof came much clanking of metal cans and a spirited rendition of a bawdy version of 'The Red Flag'. It seems Biggs *has* retained some sense of humour. Bearing in mind what followed, he needed it.

'We've missed it,' I said.

'How can we miss it? It's on the sea,' said Patel. 'If we'd missed it we'd be wet.'

'I don't care how, I just know that Brighton is further than Lumpton. We've missed it.'

'I can't be expected to drive this great brute of a van around all day, you know. It's not fair, George.'

'Well, you shouldn't have missed it.'

We had another go. We went to Chichester, Arundel, Portsmouth (again), Brighton (again) and Newhaven . . . once more listed in the order we visited them.

'Wouldn't it be cheaper to hire a taxi?' called Biggs from the roof.

'How would we get the tent in a taxi?' we both replied.

Biggs started singing the 'Ballad of Joe Hill'. From Newhaven we went to Worthing, without going through Brighton . . . I don't know how we managed that. We stopped in Worthing to let Biggs have another pee and we hammered at the door of a chippy for some supper.

'Fancy shutting a chippy on Friday night!' said Patel.

A policeman, attracted by the drunken Biggs's singing, came over and told us it was 3 a.m. and if we didn't keep quiet he'd run us all in. Then Patel went to drive the van and the policeman said we were all drunk and he'd run us in anyway. Neither Patel nor myself had touched a drop but we couldn't convince him and he did run us in. Biggs thought it was great fun.

When we proved we hadn't drunk alcohol the police thought we'd been glue-sniffing.

'We're responsible people,' I said, 'I'm an HOD, he's a local government employee and he,' pointing at Biggs, who was sprawled in a corner, 'works in a bank.'

'A likely story,' said the policeman.

'We're only here to play cricket.'

'Do I look that stupid?' said the policeman.

*

We arrived at our campsite at dawn. Birds were singing, cattle lowing. We dragged the tent out and made a half-hearted attempt at putting it up, then slept in the back of the van. We were woken at ten by Rudi.

'I'm glad I've found you . . . why 'aven't you put the tent up?'

We were all too far gone to explain. The four of us spent the next hour putting the tent up. It was very old and very musty and was clearly ex-army. I should think that in another incarnation it had housed all of Monty's staff, or two squadrons of RAF types, or an infantry battalion. Since the war it's probably been reserved as the winter home of Jerry Cottle's Circus, or is dragged out on rainy days so that Badminton gymkhana can be held under its awnings.

The tent was *huge*.

'Coo,' said Biggs, 'it's massive.'

It covered half the field. Later the farmer came down to claim his rent.

'That's a whopper, ain't it.'

Then Albert turned up with Patch . . . it seems dogs aren't allowed in the hotel.

'That's a very big tent you've got there, George,' he said.

'*I* haven't got it. *Patel* has.'

'It's still big, George.'

He tied his dog to a tent peg and set about cooking breakfast with Rudi while we three went to find some washing facilities. Rudi had come, he said, because he couldn't take the bacon breakfasts at the hotel any more.

'Solidarity, eh?' said Patel.

'No . . . the bacon's too fatty. I've brought my own,' said Rudi.

We washed in bowls from a cold water pump in a muddy farmyard. It was the sort of place that had you fumbling for the tetanus booster as soon as you clapped eyes on it. One twinge of cramp in the thumb and I'll be down the infirmary like a shot from a gun.

When we came back, the tent was on the ground and the dog had disappeared.

'Patch pulled it over,' said Albert.

Well, he may have done. I for one found it hard to believe, looking at the great big tent and thinking about the little three-legged mongrel. Rudi was wriggling on the ground, helpless with laughter. The bacon was burned.

We set off for the match with empty bellies. We'd put the tent up again but lost the dog. I for one wouldn't have minded losing both.

*

10.15 p.m. Drinking in The Red Cow, Little Lumpton-on-sea. A good day's cricket . . . i.e. we won, if only in the nick of time. With two overs to go young Carl Norton took the last two wickets with consecutive balls. Such a fine performance has moderated the distaste some of us feel for the fact that he's brought Maddy Spaight here for what seems like an extended dirty weekend. I mentioned this to Patel over supper.

'I don't care what he does,' he said.

Biggs's attitude was similar.

'Hardly my business, George. As long as he doesn't bring her into our tent, eh?'

George Jolly simply laughed. Then he asked if he might stay with us.

'Bit of an altercation with madam,' he said.

'Is Elspeth here?'

'Good God, *no*, man! Use your brain. I mean the lady of the hotel.'

I said to Albert, 'I don't think our young friend Norton is behaving as well as he might, do you?'

He said he thought I was miffed because I didn't get a bat

172

today. I'm not! Well . . . even if I were I wouldn't let it get to
me like that. I just think he's letting the side down, that's all.

Ah well, to bed after a beery supper and let's see what
tomorrow brings.

Sunday 7th August
Was awoken at 2 a.m. by Carl Norton and Maddy Spaight.
Could we put them up for the night? Honestly! What could
we say but yes? They could have erected an entire inner tent
in the far corner of our marquee and we wouldn't have
known — but for the noise. Patel seems sure that with
discretion and blankets we will not disgrace ourselves in the
morning.

'But what about them!' I said as quietly and as vehemently
as I could.

'They look like they'll be all right to me.'

He can be so naïve.

'I don't think we should encourage it,' I said.

'Go to sleep,' he said.

Carl and Maddy, I learned later, were thrown out of the
hotel because the landlady had discovered (in the middle of
the night!) that they weren't married. I don't know what sort
of altercation she'd had with our friend Jolly but it must
have been quite something to bring about this particularly
blinding vision on the road to Damascus.

*

Midday. We drove deep into the Sussex countryside to play
Old Hethers, not a school old boys' side but the name of a
village. We played between rainstorms. Patel, Tour Captain,
put me in number three to make sure I had a chance to bat. I
batted all right . . . I holed-out to a slow bowler when I was
on fifteen. I had my eye in, I just allowed my concentration
to go down the pan. Sleep deprivation, I called it. I threw my
bat when I reached the pavilion steps, too; a childish act, one
of which I don't approve in others. The match didn't even go
to a result. Rain stopped play.

We went back to Little Lumpton early. There's no sense in

driving round Sussex half-sozzled, so we bought a lot of cans from a pub and retired to our salubrious abode. Ace. I've been looking forward to this all year.

I'll ask Elizabeth to hide my cheque book when it comes to deposit-paying time this autumn for next year's tour.

*

11 p.m. The rain is bucketing down. OHCC Tour is in fact code for Sussex Monsoon season. We are playing a radio and drinking beer. Maddy and Carl smooch in a corner. Patel and Jolly are playing chess by the light of a butane lamp. I'm certain I can feel water seeping through the groundsheet. Slugs, worms, spiders and ants will visit us next, I'm sure. What a crackpot idea this was!

At about 11.30 Tommy Butcher came in with three enormous, rosy-cheeked girls.

'We were told that this is where the party is!' he cried and produced a bottle of scotch. We had our party. What else could we do? We drank and sang and snatched kisses from the enormous girls (who had names like Daisy and Maisy). At about 1 a.m. the tent collapsed and we all wriggled underneath it like children. Then the farmer came down and we discovered that Maisy and Daisy and whatever the other one was called were his daughters and he wasn't much amused.

'When I wake up I don't want that tent to be here . . . now you be off,' he said. We crawled underneath the fallen canvas and slept without attempting to put it up again in the dark.

Monday 8th August
6.30 a.m. It's surprising how cold summer mornings can be. None of us could face a trip to the pump for water — even from our far-flung meadow we could hear the altercation in the milking parlour. . . . 'An' exactly *what*, my young lady, do you think you were up to last night?' 'Oh *Dad*!' 'Nothing!' We went without breakfast. We were all tired, dirty and wet. We were all exhausted. The rain was falling again and there

would be no cricket today. We were due to be here for *three more days* including today. Impossible.

Carl Norton, George Jolly, Patel and myself rolled the tent up, prior to stuffing it in the van. Tommy Butcher was retching quietly in a corner of the field. Maddy stood in a mud-spattered blue frock. She was trying to comb her wet hair, but not having much success.

Patel chattered gaily about another place he knew where we could camp. He seemed oblivious to our surroundings. I felt as if I were battling on Flanders field.

'Where's old Jenkins gone this year?' said George Jolly.

'Spain. He said he's had enough of this,' said Patel, 'Wants sunshine . . . *here, lift that will you, be careful!* . . . on his holidays. What a fool, eh? Doesn't know how much fun he's missing.'

'Are you serious?' I said. They stood grinning at me like idiots.

'Course,' said Patel.

'Is there a station here?' I said.

'No, Worthing's the nearest.'

'I'll have to get a taxi, then.' I went and retrieved my bag from its puddle.

'I don't understand,' said Jolly.

'I think he means he's going home,' said Carl.

And I did.

'How will we get the tent back?' said Patel.

'Parcel post!' I cried from the farm's rutted track. The rain was still pouring down but I bade the farmer a very cheery farewell. My good humour lasted all the way home, even through long waits at Salisbury and Westbury for connecting services. At Salisbury I ate a cold bacon sandwich in a pub run by a miserable man and what appeared to be his even more miserable father. They didn't wipe the smile off my face, though. Oh no.

As we pulled into Mugsborough I was a happy man. I took a cab from the station. The sun was breaking through. When I arrived home there was a letter from Mugsborough College. I set it aside for Wednesday night, when I should have returned home if I'd stayed on tour. I'll save the pleasure for then, it'll do me good. I might be bored by then.

8 p.m. After a take-away curry I settled behind our patio windows to watch the summer night come down on us Mugsborians. I have locked the study, having first placed in it all things to do with work. I will not open it until Wednesday night. For the next two days I will merely sit and drink and eat and read Caesar's Gallic Wars. A nice rest. I don't even feel guilty about Patel and Hack's . . . it's their own stupid fault.

And now to *De Bello Gallico*.

Wednesday 10th August
Wandered into town this evening for a pint at The *Henry*. At eleven, on my way home, I saw Patel dashing past in his Transit. Of course he affected not to see me . . . I wasn't very surprised. I'll have to put up with this for weeks now.

11.30 p.m. Opened letter from College. '*Dear Mr Lyall, thank you for your application for the post of Head of Department (Humanities). This post has now been filled. I'm sorry you have been unsuccessful in your application and wish you every success in the future. (Signed) M.D. Channel MA per pro the Governors.*'

11.32 p.m. Opened bottle of scotch.

11.33 p.m. Decided scotch wasn't good enough. Went to garage and brought back my special bottle of single malt. I have been saving it for a grand occasion. This will do.

11.35 p.m. Opened bottle of single malt. Commenced to drink it. As if I wasn't satisfied with being depressed about the job, I went back through this diary and counted up my performances on the cricket field. It is not a pretty sight. It goes like this. . . .

2nd Jan	Abject defeat in a single wicket comp.
28th May	3 . . . bowled
5th June	0 . . . bowled
6th June	Did not bat
25th June	2 . . . l.b.w.
26th June	0 . . . not out (rain stopped play)
3rd July	18 . . . retired (Eric popped socks)

16th July	17 . . . not out
17th July	Abject defeat in a single wicket comp.
23rd July	2 . . . caught
24th July	5 . . . not out
30th July	0 . . . l.b.w.
6th Aug	Did not bat
7th Aug	15 . . . caught

Not much joy there! I have scored sixty-two runs this season and completed six innings, leaving an average of 10.333333 rep. (I leave aside single wicket comps). All that fuss, all that practice in the spring, excitement as the season approaches, disappointment on rainy days and for what? For 10.3333333 rep.

I think of myself as the sort of fellow who can take a hint, the sort who knows when the gods are against him. I'm the sort of fellow who knows when he's getting too old, and I'm thirty-nine this September.

I'm going to call it a day.

Oh god, I do hope Leonard or Maureen hasn't got that job. I couldn't take that.

Thursday 11th August

I awoke at 6.00, 9.00, 11.00 and 11.30. Finally raised myself from my pit at 11.45 approx. I've no idea what time I went to bed. Examination of the malt bottle suggests quite late. How could Coco do it? He rang at 1 p.m.

'Hullo George, back from tour? I have to talk to you.'

'I don't want to talk to you, Coco. How could you do it?'

I put the phone down.

I rang Patel.

'Hullo, Patel. Back from tour? I have to talk to you.'

'I don't want to talk to you, George. How could you do it?'

He put the phone down.

Ah well.

I take the letter to my study, lock the door firmly again and leave it. I'm not studying, reading, preparing or anything-else-ing apart from holiday-ing until September 1st. I'm not worrying about what will happen to young Norton once he's thrown on the dole queue. I'm not worrying about OHCC and how they'll manage without a secretary till the end of the season. They managed last season when the police took away Coggins, they'll manage this season — though I am not expecting a visit from the police!

No postcard from E. I suppose the Spanish post office isn't much cop. I have until Tuesday, when her ten days are up, to put on a brave face. I have until Tuesday to play Mozart tapes, drink scotch, avoid the radio and newspapers, ignore my neighbours . . . in fact I have until Tuesday to make believe I'm on a desert island. Life doesn't look so bad after all.

Tuesday 16th August

Up all Monday night doing housework. I don't know where the dirt comes from. I hoover, then polish, then hoover, then polish. I wash up, dry up, then get all the plates out of the cupboard and do them again because I've found one greasy glass. If there's a greasy glass in the house old 'hawkeye' Elizabeth will spot it.

At 7 a.m. I've just time to polish the skirting boards with my shirt cuff and lick the kitchen floor clean before I have to go for Meredith. *His* house looks like he hasn't been there for ten days. I just know Elizabeth is going to say I've made our house disgusting, filthy, unliveable. I don't know how characters like George Meredith manage it.

'How do you manage to keep it so clean, George?' I asked.

'Practice makes perfect,' he said with a straight face, hanging up his pinny and putting on his suit jacket.

We drove to Cardiff in the new yellow Metro. The plane was delayed so we had hours and hours together. He's like a block of wood.

'Good holiday?' I said.

'Mm.'

'Go out much?'

'No.'

'More coffee?'

'No thanks.'

'Have any girls round while she was away?'

'*What!*'

178

That woke him up.

When Christina came through the barrier she didn't look very pleased to see me. There she was with her arms flung round her George. On one side of them there was a line of white taffs going off to get brown, on the other a line of brown taffs come back to get white again. What ridiculous creatures we humans are!

'Where's Elizabeth?' I said.

'Didn't you get her card?' said Christina. She reddened under her tan.

'No. Where is she?'

'She's booked to stay on for a while. Her school doesn't go back for a couple of weeks and so she's decided to stay on.'

'Stay on? On her own?' This was taking quite a bit of comprehension.

'Not completely on her own . . . are you sure you haven't got her card, George?'

We were walking out to the airport car park. Meredith followed us, laden down with sombreros, cheap cognac, suitcases, plastic bags. When he tried to take a trolley a porter shouted at him.

'I'm sure,' I said. 'Who's she with?'

'Phillip Jenkins.'

I'm afraid I rather saw red. I kicked the ground, threw the car keys at Meredith who dropped all his bags and broke the cognac to catch them. Christina began to cry. I yelled something to the effect that I was fed up with driving round in a piece of fluorescent vomit, then stalked away to find a train. Not as easy as it sounds.

*

I'm fed up with puerile sports, I'm fed up with bloody women and *I'm sick to death of having to write it all down in this wretched diary!*

I'm not doing it any more.

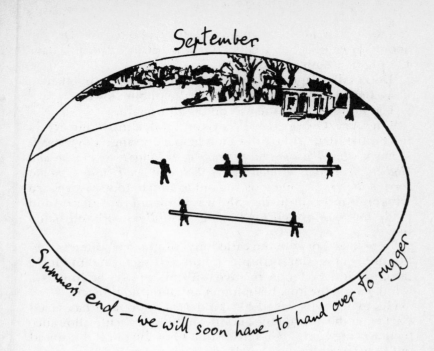

September

Summer's end — we will soon have to hand over to rugger

Monday 5th September

Though I *had* promised myself I wouldn't write in this book again, some things have happened which are worth recording.

The first is that Patel, on hearing of my . . . my problems, came round immediately and said what a stupid idea camping had been and how they'd all hated it and how they'd all thought I'd done the right thing and how they'd all missed me for the rest of the tour. Even if it wasn't true it was pretty big of him to say so. It was a white fib.

'We're staying in a three-star in Worthing next season,' he said. 'Albert's negotiated a special rate.'

'I can imagine. I hope you'll enjoy yourselves. I won't be coming, though. I've retired.'

'George, you can't.'

'I have.'

I won't be moved on that one, either.

People have been very kind.

Elizabeth moved into a bedsit in Bristol (*sans* Jenkins, of course . . . I knew that wouldn't last). I phoned the Dragon about something . . . I believe it was because I didn't have E.'s phone number.

'Don't talk to me . . . you've brought this on yourself. You *drove* her to it!' she yelled and put the phone down.

Ten minutes later she was on the line again.

'I'm sorry, George. It was crass and unfeeling of me to talk to you like that,' she said. Can a leopard change its spots? It seems it can. '*The old order changeth, yielding place to new, and God fulfils himself in many ways, Lest one good custom should corrupt the world.*' She took me out to lunch, too . . . a reborn Dragon is most confusing. She was kind and considerate and made me hate myself for having misunderstood and hated her.

Spite heard of what he called my 'plight' and came round to ramble at me for a couple of hours. It seems having led a laconic life he's fallen in love with talking. I see him as a wandering educator, blabbing at anyone who'll listen.

His ex-wife displayed her kinder side too, and has saved Carl from the dole queue and life on his minuscule allowance by marrying him . . . or at least that's how he put it. I pointed out that he could always be a part-timer again.

'No,' he said firmly, 'Maddy and I are off to seek our fortune in Fulham. I will write poetry, she will bake cakes. We will live humbly but happily.'

I don't think the new Mrs Norton needs to seek a fortune, but if that's how Carl chooses to see things I didn't want to take it on myself to puncture his dream. A sort of gentle Bohemianism won't hurt either of them, I'm sure . . . and if they get fed up Maddy can always buy them a big house somewhere and they can start again, only this time with a cook and a butler.

The new HOD here is neither Leonard nor Maureen. He's a flash harry from the north called Denis with a swagger in his walk and a pocketful of PhDs . . . two to my knowledge. How somebody that young and that much of a working-class-lad-made-good could pick up *that* much education is beyond me. I left things neat for him and he appears to appreciate it. Coco collared me today and said it was someone playing politics at county level that had lost me the job. It *might* be true, I suppose.

'Also, George,' he said, 'I don't like being referred to as "Coco".'

And he winked!

I played my last game for Hack's during the weekend . . . versus Netherpopham, a needle match, on Sunday. Brian Cook came round on Wednesday and talked me into it, he said it would be such a disappointment to retire without having a retirement game (I haven't played since the tour, and intended never to again). There was quite a crowd up there and they saw a well-fought match. Netherpopham produced their usual crop of confusing and unlikely players, a verger who looks like a vicar, a vicar who looks like a squire (red cheeks and bushy sideburns), a postman who looks like a postmistress, a slim publican (!) and three teenagers one of whom was the fastest bowler I've ever faced. When I was batting with Tommy Butcher he (Tommy) came down the track and said, 'How are you dealing with him?'

'I'm not,' I said, 'I'm just putting my leg and bat roughly where I reckon the ball should be.'

Which was true. We won with three wickets in hand, having been set 119 before tea (they declared at tea, as is usual).

Oh yes . . . and I was 25 not out at the end. *That's* really why I re-opened this diary. I split my bat, too.

'I bet you won't retire now!' called Cooky. It would be tempting. With that foul creature Jenkins gone, with no more HOD-type worries, no wife to bend my ear . . . it's tempting. But my decision is made. Albert says he'll get me elected an Honorary Vice-President. He made it sound as if I'd be the only one, not one of the thirty already in office.

I'll just devote myself to teaching, I think. As long as the white-coated men in the Mercedes ambulance don't come for me I'll consider myself a success. I'll even be able to go and watch Test Matches next year, now that I'm not playing any more. Super.

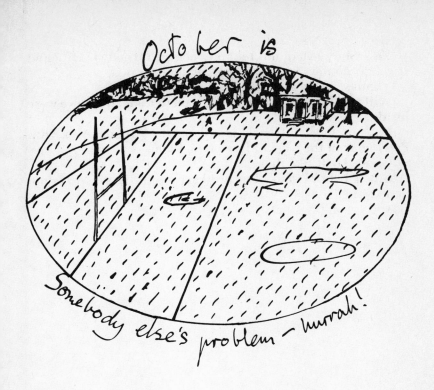

October is Somebody else's problem — hurrah!

Sunday 2nd October
Elizabeth came round. It's her first visit. She's swapped the disgusting yellow Metro for a Maestro. It seems Eric had left her some money.

'*Hasn't* it rained?' she said.

'Oh yes it's rained,' I said.

'*Hasn't* it been a wet September?' she said.

'All round,' I said.

'How's College?' she said.

'Okay,' I said. 'How's school?'

'Okay. I've brought you a birthday present. It's in the car.'

'I had your card last week,' I said. 'Thanks.'

We went out to her car.

'Patel helped me choose it. He said you'd broken the other.'

It was a Polyplastic Duncan Fearnley. The right length, too.

185

'How kind.' I said.

'Yes.' She smiled and took my arm. I turned sharply and saw a dozen net curtains being hastily dropped.

'Thanks.'

'Will you play next season?' Elizabeth asked when we were inside.

'I'm not sure. I'll try this out on the Missile Area with Patel later in the week. I'll see how I feel.'

'Good. He'll like that.'

'But if I do,' I said, 'I'm not keeping a diary . . . it's too depressing.'

And I won't.